NATURAL DISASTERS

NATURAL DISASTERS

RICHARD O'NEILL

Picture credits:

USGS Photographic Library: pages 6 *(top)*,
7 *(top)*, 14, 15, 21, 22, 23, 24, 25, 26, 27, 28,
29, 30, 31, 42, 43, 44, 44-45, 45 *(below)*,
55 *(top right)*, 55 *(below right)*, 82 *(right)*, 83.

E.T. Archive: pages 9, 16, 17 *(top)*, 17
(below), 19, 35 *(below)*, 36, 37, 39, 46-47, 51,
63 *(below left)*, 66-67, 86, 88, 90, 92, 93 *(top)*,
93 *(below)*, 94, 95.

Kent County Council: pages 64, 65.

With thanks to Antoni Daszewski of The
Antique Print Shop, East Grinstead, West
Sussex, for supplying many of the engravings
reproduced in this book.

CONTENTS

INTRODUCTION

THE BRITISH biologist James E. Lovelock put forward an idea now accepted by many New Age enthusiasts in his famous book *Gaia: A New Look at Life on Earth*, published in 1979. According to Lovelock's 'Gaia hypothesis', the planet Earth (named Gaia, after the Earth Mother goddess of the Ancient Greeks, at the suggestion of Nobel prize-winning novelist William Golding) is a living organism. The human race, along with all other living things, has an interdependent relationship with Gaia: she gives us the means of life; in return, we must safeguard her ecological balance.

Lovelock suggested that Gaia embodies various self-regulating processes – for example, maintaining an unchanging oxygen-methane balance in the atmosphere – but did not suggest that the planet has developed conscious mechanisms intended to ensure its survival. Some of his more enthusiastic followers, however, believe that Gaia, faced with potentially deadly 'diseases' stemming from humanity's ecological crimes, acts just like a sick person: she takes measures to destroy the sources of infection.

A far-fetched notion, perhaps? But when one considers the many efforts that Gaia has made to bury, burn, drown or otherwise destroy her human tormentors – by earthquake, volcanic eruption, flood, drought, plague, and other natural disasters – it is not impossible to suspect that, like Dean Swift's giant king in *Gulliver's Travels*, Gaia may regard us as 'nasty little vermin…crawling across the planet's face.'

The disastrous impact on the natural world made by humankind, especially since the Industrial Revolution of the

1700s-1800s, may trigger off greatly increased hostile action by Gaia. Before the Industrial Revolution, Earth's atmosphere was estimated to contain about 275 parts per million (ppm) of carbon dioxide: by 1990, the proportion had risen to around 350 ppm. Many scientists see this rise, caused by the vastly increased consumption of fossil fuels (coal, oil, natural gas), deforestation and the concomitant burning of wood, and the emission by modern agricultural and manufacturing processes of other 'greenhouse gases', as a major contributor to the 'greenhouse effect', a significant rise in Earth's temperature ('global warming').

ATMOSPHERIC WARMING

A report in 1997, backed by the British Meteorological Office, stated that the year was the world's hottest since the accurate registration of global records began in the 1860s, and that the five previous hottest years had all occurred *since 1990*. Although this was partly attributable to the unusual surge of El Niño, the great warm current of the

Viewed from space (below right), Earth appears to be tranquil – but powerful forces seethe below Mother Gaia's crust, and often break through (above).

Earth's volcanoes are sited near seas. Rising water erodes the volcanoes' sides until they are unable to withstand the pressure of the molten rock within – and the volcano explodes. The eruption of the Soufriere Hills volcano, which devastated Montserrat in mid-1997, may have owed much to this cause. The formation of new volcanoes, like the recently discovered Columbo on the Mediterranean seabed north of Crete, and the stimulation of currently dormant ones presents something worse than an immediate threat to the lives of those living near them. A sudden burst of eruptions might fill the atmosphere with such vast quantities of ash as to block sunlight sufficiently to cause a new Ice Age; or, alternatively, release greenhouse gases that would significantly accelerate global warming. Even on a lesser scale, the eruptions' effect on air quality could cause millions of deaths from respiratory illnesses.

It is a regrettable fact of human nature that we often take a kind of pleasure in contemplating, from a safe distance, the misfortunes of others. But as you read the catalogue of natural disasters presented here, beware of thinking, 'it will never happen to me'. Perhaps it would be safer to consider how best to make your peace with Gaia!

7

Pacific Ocean, and to erratic increases in the Sun's output of radiation, the report concluded that 'the human-made increase in atmospheric greenhouse gases is the only known mechanism which can explain the observed long-term lower atmospheric warming.'

The report predicted that the rise in global temperatures in the 21st century might be as high as 3°C (5.4°F). If this should happen, sea level rises would put some 30 million persons (notably in the coastal areas of Africa, the eastern Mediterranean, China and Japan, India and the East Indies, the south-eastern United States and Central America) in yearly danger of floods that would dwarf the worst inundations (except the Biblical Deluge) described in this book.

AN EXPLOSIVE AGE

British scientists, including professors of geology at Oxford and London Universities, have warned that rises in sea-level caused by icecaps melting as a result of global warming could usher in an 'explosive age'. Some 90 per cent of

ACTS OF GOD

IN LEGAL terminology, a happening beyond human control, such as a flood, cyclone or earthquake, is an 'Act of God'. Thus, it seems appropriate that this collection of disasters should begin by examining two events that, to Christian believers, are truly acts of God: Noah's Flood and the Plagues of Egypt.

The Book of Genesis tells how God, angered by humanity's wickedness, determined to destroy 'all flesh' on Earth. Only the 'righteous man' Noah, with his family, was preserved, to repopulate the cleansed Earth. God ordered Noah to build a ship (ark) to accommodate himself, his wife, his three sons and their wives, and a breeding pair of every bird and beast. The ark's measurements as specified in Genesis – 300 cubits long, 50 cubits wide, 30 cubits high; or approximately 152m (500ft) x 24m (80ft) x 15m (50ft) – hardly seem to denote a vessel large enough to transport an estimated 100,000 animals.

A WORLDWIDE FLOOD

On Sunday 7 December 2349 BC, according to the chronology of Archbishop James Ussher (1581–1656), there began 40 days of rain, resulting in a worldwide flood. When the waters receded, the Ark made landfall (on Wednesday 6 May 2348 BC, says Ussher) on Mount Ararat (in eastern Turkey). Noah sacrificed to God, who promised never again to destroy all living creatures, setting a 'bow' (usually interpreted as the rainbow) in the sky to seal the covenant.

Universal floods sent as a divine punishment feature in the legends of many regions, including Central America

and China. Did such a flood really occur? Archaeological evidence shows that a great flood struck the city of Ur, in the

Mesopotamian basin that was the cradle of civilization, around 3500 BC. This is commemorated in the *Epic of Gilgamesh* (c.2500 BC), in which a Babylonian Noah called Utnapishtim saves his family and some beasts by building an ark that eventually comes to rest on a mountain. Ur was the original home of Abraham, and the Biblical story may stem, like the *Gilgamesh* epic, from its destruction. However, some scientists believe that

Above: Only Noah and his family survived God's great flood that punished the world.

9

Above: The Great Day of His Wrath – a painting depicting the Day of Judgement.

there was a truly universal flood about 12,000–10,000 years ago, when a melt-down of the North American ice cap caused a dramatic rise in sea-levels worldwide, forcing all living things to move far inland.

The Book of Exodus describes how God's anger was provoked when the Pharaoh of Egypt refused to free the enslaved Israelites. Acting through his prophets Moses and Aaron, God struck the Egyptians with ten 'plagues' (according to Exodus; only seven according to Psalm 105). First, the waters of the Nile turned to blood. Non-believers point out that this phenomenon is still occasionally seen, when volcanic detritus and algae from the Blue and White Niles give the waters of the Delta a red hue. The second (frogs), third (lice), fourth (flies), fifth (cattle disease), sixth (boils), seventh (hail, which destroys the crops), and eighth (locusts) plagues are all explainable in terms of natural disasters. The ninth plague, three days of total darkness, may stem from the *Khamsin* gales: blowing from the Sahara, these often darken Egypt's skies with thick dust clouds in March.

The tenth plague, the death in a single night of all the first-born of Egypt, human and animal alike, perhaps stems from folk memories of a sudden and deadly epidemic. The Jewish festival of Passover commemorates this act of God, for the wrath of the Lord 'passed over' the Israelites, whose dwellings were marked by the blood of a sacrificial lamb or kid goat.

SEEKING THE LOST ARK

Reports of 'ship's timbers' on or near Mount Ararat date back to 275 BC, but various expeditions in search of Noah's ark have had little result. Ark-hunting seemed set for revival in 1997, when America's Central Intelligence Agency (CIA) released several thousand photographs, taken by U-2 spyplanes in the 1960s–70s, of the 'Ararat Anomaly', apparently a boat-shaped object embedded in Ararat's ice-cap. Biblical fundament-alists claimed that this, at last, was the true Ark – but CIA sources hint that later satellite pictures, still classified, show that it is merely a geological formation.

EARTH'S LONG, COLD NIGHT

EARTH IS under constant bombardment. Many thousand meteoroids (properly, the term 'meteor' applies only to the 'shooting star' seen when one of these pieces of cosmic debris burns up on entering Earth's atmosphere) hurtle towards our planet every day. Most are mere grains of dust, but larger meteoroids (above 1kg/2.2lb in weight), or fragments of them, sometimes survive the friction of the atmosphere to strike Earth as meteorites.

The largest meteorite to have landed intact (in southern Africa) is the 60-tonne Hoba West specimen. But it is certain that much larger meteorites have impacted with Earth in the past. The largest crater that can *definitely* be attributed to a meteor strike, of relatively recent date, is the variously named Meteor, Barringer or Canyon Diablo Crater in the Arizona desert. Here, some 25,000 years ago, a meteor exploded with the force of a 30-megaton hydrogen bomb, blasting out a crater 1.6km (1mi) wide and 174m (570ft) deep. It is a comfort to know that scientists estimate that only three meteorites large enough to cause a crater up to 10km (6mi) will strike Earth every 1,000,000 years – and that two of these will land in the oceans.

METEORITE STRIKE

Some 65,000,000 years ago, Earth may have experienced its most devastating meteorite strike. It wiped out the creatures that had dominated the planet for 160,000,000 years, throughout the Triassic, Jurassic and Cretaceous periods – the dinosaurs. It is theorized that a meteorite (or, some scientists say, an asteroid or the head of a comet) about 10km (6.25mi) in diameter struck in Central America, where its impact is marked by the 200km (124mi)-wide Chicxulub Crater on Mexico's Yucatán

Above: Some scientists believe that massive lava flows led to the extinction of the dinosaurs.

Peninsula. Its detonation hurled so much stony debris into the atmosphere that the skies were obscured for many months, causing a long, freezing night in which the dinosaurs, and other species, died of hunger, since all plant vegetation withered away, and cold.

FLOODS OF LAVA

Not all scientists agree with this theory. Some believe the extinction of the dinosaurs was caused by 'basalt floods', massive outpourings of lava from the volcanic action that formed India's Deccan Plateau at around the same time the Chicxulub Crater was made. The gases these released may have had the same effect as the Chicxulub strike. Others believe the dinosaurs' demise was a much more prolonged process, possibly caused by progressive changes in climate, again because of volcanic action, in ocean levels and currents, or in the distribution of vegetation.

Whatever the cause, bad luck for the dinosaurs was good news for mammals – including eventually the latecomer, humankind which were able to take the reptiles' place in the recovering ecology.

But will the mammals' reign last as long as that of their predecessors? It is estimated that once every 100,000,000 years, a meteor or asteroid with a diameter of 10km (6mi) will strike Earth. Such an impact would lead to mass extinction. There may be some 1,100 bodies of significant size (that is, weighing in excess of some 35kg/77lb) in Earth-crossing orbits – and

Above: A strike from a comet head would bring devastation to Earth.

observatories worldwide keep a routine watch for them. And it is not only professional doom mongers who advocate that ballistic-missile technology should be developed to the point where humanity is capable of destroying or deflecting any threat from space.

11

FIRE FROM HEAVEN

The only substantiated case of human deaths caused by a meteor strike was recorded as recently as December 1997. In a village near Bogotá, Colombia, blazing debris from a meteorite set fire to a house, burning to death four small children. Only one person is recorded as being struck by a meteorite: a woman in Alabama, who suffered severe bruising when a 4kg (9lb) body crashed through her roof.

GREAT BALLS OF FIRE

'EVERYTHING started to shake…we thought the Earth was caving in,' said 96-year-old Grigory Verkhoturov to a TV interviewer in 1997. As a child, Verkhoturov had experienced the 'Tunguska event' of 30 June 1908, and remembered how, more than 80km (50mi) from the explosion, buildings rocked and folk were thrown to the ground – rising only to their knees to pray for mercy on the Day of Judgment.

Like the passing of the dinosaurs (pages 10-11), the monstrous explosion near the Tunguska River, Siberia, was probably caused by cosmic debris. Many scientists think that the disintegration in Earth's atmosphere of a small comet or comet-fragment produced a blast and fireball equal to those released by an H-bomb.

Some 6,480 hectares (25sq mi) of forest was flattened; it is estimated that no living thing within about 50km (30mi) survived. A few nomadic herdsmen may have died: one far enough from the fireball to escape with superficial burns reported that his 1,500 reindeer, nearer the blast, had vanished without trace.

Intense heat melted the Siberian permafrost, causing severe flooding. The blast was heard 800km (500mi) away; shock waves, severe enough to halt a train on the Trans-Siberian Railway, 600km (375mi) south, registered on a major earthquake scale in London and New York.

A VIOLENT EXPLOSION

Some scientists attribute the destruction to a fragment, no more than 50m (165ft) in diameter, from Encke's Comet, which visits Earth every 3.3 years. The violence of the explosion was due not to the fragment's size, but to its relative velocity to that of Earth. A 10-tonne fragment travelling at 50km/sec (540,000mph) has kinetic energy equal to 10,000 tonnes of high-explosive TNT. The Tunguska fragment's explosion, perhaps 5km (3mi) above Earth, has been estimated as equivalent to 30,000,000 tonnes of TNT.

A comet may appear enormous, for its tail and coma (surrounding the nucleus)

Above: It is possible that a fragment from a disintegrating comet caused the 'Tunguska event'.

ODDBALL THEORIES

The lunatic fringe insists that the Tunguska explosion was caused by the explosion of the atomic power-plant of an alien spaceship. The heroic aliens, they say, deliberately steered their doomed craft into one of Earth's least populated areas. Slightly more respectable are theories that it was caused by an intrusion of 'anti-matter', or by the action of a 'black hole'.

may extend over many thousands of kilometres, but these are only gas and dust. Its solid nucleus, a frozen mass of rock particles, water, ammonia and methane, is small: that of the great Halley's Comet is only about 15km x 10km (9mi x 6mi).

Considering what the result of a Tunguska-sized fragment striking a densely-populated area would be – and judging from satellite photographs of massive scars on Jupiter caused by the impact of comet Shoemaker-Levy 9 in 1994 – it is not surprising that humanity has always feared comets. Since antiquity, when the Greeks named them *kometes* ('hairy stars'), their appearance has been said to foretell plague, famine, war and other disasters. Halley's Comet, on various visits (it appears every 76

Above: Earth is under constant bombardment from meteoroids, comets, asteroids and a wide variety of space dust and debris.

years), was said to foreshadow the fall of Jerusalem in AD 70, the defeat of Attila the Hun in 451, and the Norman victory at the Battle of Hastings in 1066. It appears in the Baycux Tapestry, where cowering Anglo-Saxons are shown with the legend 'They fear the star'. In 1456, the Pope, blaming it for a Turkish onslaught on Belgrade, denounced it as an agent of Satan. On its visit in 1910, Chicago witnessed a panic when a popular newspaper suggested that Earth's passage through its tail would wipe out millions by cyanogen-gas poisoning. In fact, our planet has often passed through comets' tails without harm.

EVOLUTIONARY SPECULATION

A theory propounded by the distinguished astronomers Sir Fred Hoyle (b.1915) and Chandra Wickramasinghe is that life on Earth may have begun as a result of 'seeding' from space: basic life forms may have developed within the nucleus of a comet that struck Earth billions of years ago. Nobel Prize winner Frances Crick (b.1916), co-cracker of the DNA code, believes comets may have contributed to life on Earth by delivering essential amino acids and other molecules from outer space.

SOMETHING'S GOT TO GIVE

EARTH'S THIN crust consists of around twelve large plates and several lesser ones, between 30-240km (20-150mi) thick, that 'drift' at the rate of about 1mm (0.04in) per week on the 'sea' of molten rock and metal below. This 'continental drift' has resulted in the formation of land masses, in the creation of mountains and volcanoes-and in the mighty shudders called plate tectonic earthquakes.

Tectonic earthquakes are the result of two plates grinding against each other as they move in different directions. They become locked by friction, and for many years may not move at all – but all that time immense pressures are building up. When the pressure reaches critical intensity, the locked plates may 'slip' or 'jump', causing an earthquake. (Volcanic earthquakes, usually much less severe than tectonic shocks, are dealt with on pages 30-31 *et seq*; human-induced earthquakes can be caused by underground nuclear weapons' testing, the collapse of mine galleries, and similar happenings.)

The areas along the borders of interlocked plates form 'fault lines' (like the notorious San Andreas Fault, see pages 28-29) where earthquakes are most likely to occur. The American geologist David Simpson puts it simply: 'Whenever pressure builds up for a long time…something's got to give!'

One fault area lies off the Pacific coast of Mexico, where the oceanic Cocos Plate, moving northeast, impacts with the continental North American Plate, moving west. Although Mexico did not experience a major tremor for many years, geologists, noting that surrounding regions had been troubled, were so sure that the 'Michoacan seismic gap' (i.e., an area where seismometers, that measure movement of the Earth, had registered little activity for decades) would undergo a severe earthquake that state-of-the-art seismological instruments were deployed in the area. 'It will be the best-recorded major quake ever,' predicted one seismologist.

EARTHQUAKE DEVASTATION

The scientists' expectations were fulfilled on 18 September 1985 when, beginning at 0718 hours, a 120-second upheaval, registering 8.1 on the 1-10 Richter Scale that measures the severity of earthquakes, devastated Mexico City, one of the

Left: Ranking high at 8.1 on the Richter Scale, a two-minute shock tore apart Mexico City on 18 September 1985. Above: The San Andreas Fault, and a number of smaller faults, threaten California with earthquakes. This shock at San Fernando in 1971 brought down a highway overpass.

Left: A further view of the destruction caused by the San Fernando earthquake in 1971. Above: A severe tremor gutted this house at Charleston, South Carolina, on 13 August 1886. Below: Piled debris in the wake of the Mexico City quake.

15

world's most densely populated urban areas. Some 500 buildings collapsed immediately. Among these was the seven-storey gynaecology-obstetrics wing of the General Hospital, housing some 280 patients and staff. Almost all were killed – but a 'miracle' followed. Seven days later, a tiny baby (identified as the daughter of Crisanta Nuñez, whose body was never found) was dug alive from the ruins. Loss of life in the fall of the 12-storey Juárez Hospital was even greater: some 600 of its 1,000 occupants died. The Nueva León apartment building became what the media called 'a collective tomb' for more than 1,000 persons.

around 5,500 killed, 40,000 injured and more than 30,000 homeless.

Many of the fallen buildings were specifically designed to withstand earthquakes. But Mexico City stands on a bed of soft sediment left by an ancient lake, and subsidence of up to 25cm (10in) annually weakens foundations. So the city reacted to the shock, said an American expert, 'like a bowl of jelly'. Although some damage and fatalities were incurred in coastal regions within about 80km (50mi) of the quakes' offshore epicentre (some 320km/200mi southwest of Mexico City) , the coastal towns' rocky foundations provided better resistance to the tremors.

MASS PANIC

Thirty-six hours after the first quake, as official and volunteer rescue crews strove to dig out the thousands buried under the rubble, a 60-second shock registering 7.5 on the Richter Scale struck. More buildings, already damaged, fell, and mass panic among the citizens was only narrowly averted. Some 10,000 soldiers were brought in to preserve public order and prevent looting. The final toll was

SOMETHING TO BE THANKFUL FOR

Some survivors of the Mexico City quake reacted in stereotypical ways. An American was dramatic: 'The building swayed five or six feet each way... It would go all the way one way and you'd think it was going over... Next time it would sway all the way the other way and you'd think it would crash,' said a businessman on the tenth floor of an hotel. A Briton was phlegmatic: 'I looked out of the window and saw a building collapse. I turned to my wife and said, 'I think we've got a slight earth tremor.' And a Mexican cabdriver, told that tax offices were among government buildings destroyed, said: 'Maybe there is a God.'

SHOCKS FOR THE ROMAN EMPIRE

LIKE THEIR pagan neighbours, the Christians of the Roman Empire believed that natural disasters were a manifestation of divine wrath. Thus, when earthquakes racked 'the greater part of the Roman world' (says the historian Edward Gibbon) in AD 365, pagans and Christians alike blamed the destruction on their neighbours' impiety.

On 21 July of that year, massive undersea upheavals shook cities all around the Mediterranean coastline and triggered tsunami (tidal waves; see pages 44-45 *et seq*) that threatened to overwhelm them. The people of Epidaurus, on the Greek coast, attributed their preservation to the holiness of St. Hilarion: the aged monk is said to have quelled approaching waves by making the sign of the cross. On the Egyptian coast, the inhabitants of Alexandria- despite the fact that it was a leading centre of Christianity – were less fortunate.

THE ROARING SEA

The first results of the undersea quake were beneficial: the Mediterranean's waters retreated so far that folk were able to wade out and catch an abundance of fish with their bare hands. But then, wrote an eyewitness, 'the roaring sea…rose in its turn…[and] dashed mightily upon islands and broad stretches of the mainland.' Of an estimated 100,000 persons killed by the shocks of 21 July, some 50,000 perished in Alexandria alone, most by drowning. Damage to buildings in the great city, with its palaces and famous library, was less severe: the Pharos, the c.110m (350ft)-high lighthouse built in 280 BC, one of the Seven Wonders of the Ancient World, survived near-intact.

Mediterranean Christians suffered another severe blow in 526 AD, when an earthquake on the evening of 29 May almost totally destroyed the city of Antioch. Then one of the major cities of the Eastern Roman Empire, situated about 32km (20mi) inland from the Mediterranean coast of Syria, Antioch was a true metropolis, even boasting a system of oil-fired street lighting. A rapid succession of shocks brought down most buildings within minutes; fire spread quickly through the ruins, and many who

Above: Roman military might – represented here on a pavement mosaic dating from around 100 AD – was of no avail against earthquakes and floods.

16

THE LONG-LIVED LIGHTHOUSE

Having survived the earthquake of AD 365 (and storm damage in 793), Alexandria's Pharos lighthouse was at last levelled about one millennium later, by yet another earthquake in 1346. Another of the Seven Wonders to fall to an earthquake was the Colossus of Rhodes, a giant bronze figure of the sun god Helios. Legend says it was more that 30m (100ft) tall, and straddled the harbour entrance at Rhodes so that ships entered between its legs. In fact, it was almost certainly smaller, and stood beside the harbour.

Below: The scene after an earthquake in Calabria, in October 1905.

Bottom: A map of the Mediterranean showing seismic areas of the Neapolitan earthquake in December 1857.

had escaped being crushed now perished through burning or suffocation. Other survivors were murdered by the gangs of outlaws from the surrounding countryside who swarmed in to loot among the rubble. The death toll is estimated at between 250,000 and 300,000.

The authorities sought to avert Antioch's 'plague' of earthquakes (an earlier catastrophe, in 115 AD, had been blamed on the Christians and resulted in the martyrdom of its bishop, St. Ignatius,

THE REMAINS OF ANTIOCH

In the early days of Christianity, Antioch's religious importance was equivalent to that of Rome today, for 'it was in Antioch that the disciples were first called Christians' (*Acts*; Chapter 11, Verse 26), after St. Paul's ministry there. Among the treasures excavated at Antioch, where the remains of the ancient walls, aqueduct, theatre, fortress and other buildings are still to be seen, was the 'Antioch Chalice', now in the Metropolitan Museum of Art, New York, which on its discovery in c.1910 was claimed by some to be the Holy Grail. It has since been dated as work of the 6th century AD – so it may well have survived the earthquake of 526.

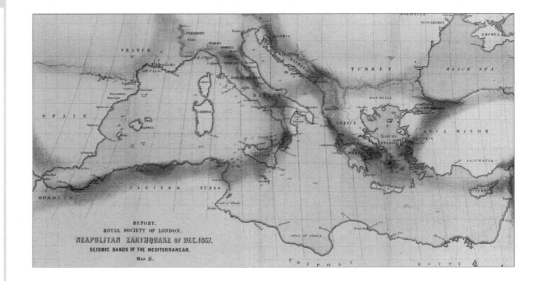

REPORT.
ROYAL SOCIETY OF LONDON.
NEAPOLITAN EARTHQUAKE OF DEC. 1857.
SEISMIC BANDS OF THE MEDITERRANEAN.
MAP D.

at the order of Emperor Trajan; an earthquake in 528, just as the city was being rebuilt, killed a further 5,000 persons) by changing its name to Theopolis ('City of God'). It didn't

work: the city, now Antakya, Turkey, and only a fraction of its ancient size, has suffered regularly from severe shocks, the most destructive of recent times being in 1872.

17

BIG TROUBLE IN CHINA

CHINESE philosophy holds that natural disasters such as earthquakes are sent by the gods. If that is so, the providence that watches over the Chinese people is fickle, for the country has experienced some of the most destructive earthquakes, floods and famines in recorded history.

Since early times, high population density in China has meant that earthquakes tend to cause an horrific death toll. The earthquake which hit Shensi on 2 February 1556 is believed to have killed more people than any other in recorded history: an estimated 820,000. The local people lived in the most vulnerable of homes: artificial caves carved out of cliff-sides, which came crashing down with their occupants. On 16 December 1920, China suffered another major quake in Kansu. About 200,000 people were killed directly, and the winter chill claimed a further 20,000 who were left homeless and simply froze to death. The same region suffered another earthquake in 1932, which killed 70,000. At Nan-shan, on 22 May 1927, 200,000 were killed.

A VIOLENT EARTHQUAKE

On 28 July 1976, China suffered its worst earthquake for four centuries, almost directly underneath the densely-populated city of Tang-shan. The violent quake hit the city at night, when most of its 1,000,000 inhabitants lay defenceless in their beds. The official death toll, published three years later, was set at 242,000, with thousands more seriously injured; unofficial estimates range as high as 750,000 dead. The violence of the quake hurled people 2m (6ft) into the air, and within a matter of seconds 95 per cent of Tang-shan had collapsed into rubble. The earth split open into wide fissures and thousands of sink-holes, trees were uprooted and railroad tracks buckled. Amazingly, coal-miners working in the solid rock deep below Tang-shan survived the violent shaking that razed the city above them.

One of the lucky survivors, Tang-shan police officer Ho Shu-shen, described how it all began. Wakened by 'a strong wind blowing dust and light rain', he saw 'a quick flash of greenish-blue light in the sky' – a multi-coloured light show which was visible 320km (200mi) away from the doomed city. There was a rumbling, 'like the noise of a freight train', then moments later the earth shook. Ho managed to jump out of his window just before his house collapsed like a pack of cards.

MAJOR AFTERSHOCKS

The quake lasted only 23 seconds. Its effects were felt across 320km (200mi) of northeastern China, tumbling older buildings in several cities, causing millions of dollars' worth of damage and killing 100 people in the capital, Beijing. In the next two days, more than 125 major aftershocks were experienced across the region. A massive relief effort brought in rescue workers, emergency supplies and medical personnel; it was three years before the government began rebuilding the shattered city.

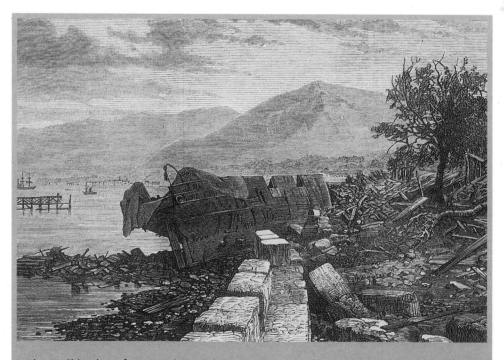

Above: China has often experienced destructive earthquakes, typhoons, floods and famine.

18

DRAGONS AND TOADS

Although Chinese traditional belief holds the gods responsible for natural disasters, it was a Chinese scholar who made the first scientific attempt to track down the source of earthquakes. In AD 132, the sage Chang Heng, reasoning that waves must ripple through the earth from the quake's source, constructed his own detector. This was a large bronze pot, with eight dragons' heads around the rim, each holding a delicately balanced ball in its mouth, and with open-mouthed bronze toads seated below. Ground tremors would make the dragon on the side nearest to them drop its ball to the toad below, indicating the direction of the quake. Today China remains among the world leaders (with Japan, Russia and the USA) in researching earthquake prediction. In 1975, Chinese scientists acted on reports of unusual animal behaviour successfully to predict a quake at Haicheng, evacuating 90,000 residents just two days before the quake wrecked 90 per cent of the city's buildings.

Below: With its high density of population, China has suffered from terrible loss of life due to devastating earthquakes throughout its recorded history.

THE TRIPLE TERROR OF LISBON

THE EARTHQUAKE that struck Lisbon on 1 November 1755, lasted for only seven minutes, but was certainly one of the most powerful in recorded history. It was, however, only one of the three terrors that destroyed Portugal's major city, claiming an estimated 100,000 victims from a population of some 250,000 persons.

The earth began to shake at 0930 hours, when people who had congregated in the city's many splendid churches for the major feast of All Saints' Day first saw candles and crucifixes topple from the altars, then watched in horror as walls began to buckle. A captain aboard his ship in the bay told afterwards how he watched dumbstruck as the city's stone buildings swayed 'like a wheat field in a breeze'.

LISBON LAY IN RUINS

The second, and major, shock came 40 minutes later. It shook all Portugal, and much of Spain and Morocco, and was felt across western Europe, raising waves on Loch Ness in Scotland and ripping boats from their moorings in Amsterdam. In seconds much of Lisbon lay in ruins: British surgeon Richard Wolsall reported that in 'about the tenth part of a minute' the quake toppled 'every church and convent in town, together with the King's palace and the magnificent opera-house…there was not a large building in town that escaped.' Some 18,000 buildings toppled; a 5m (16ft) fissure split the centre of the city. Hundreds were buried under falling masonry. The scene was a nightmare of dead bodies, screaming injured and trapped victims,

and panic-stricken survivors fleeing for the safety of open space.

Within a short time, when thousands had fled the city and gathered for safety on the quay of the River Tagus, the sea joined in the act of destruction. A huge wave (tsunami) triggered by the earthquake surged up 12m (40ft) above sea level. All the refugees on the quay were swept away and drowned, while the water crashed down to flood the lower half of the city. Less than an hour later, tidal waves broke over the walls of Cadiz in Spain, and surged on to hit Gibraltar, the Moroccan coast and the island of Madeira.

Back in Lisbon, around noon, overturned lamps and abandoned cooking-fires added fire to the assault of earth and water. The blaze raged with such fury that after three days the remains of the city were 'reduced to cinders'. Many who had survived falling masonry died in the flames. Those who had survived all these horrors and remained in the shattered city still had to face powerful aftershocks, a scarcity of food even more life-threatening than lack of shelter, and the violence of looters who moved in like vultures to pick over the ruins.

The Portuguese king and his government sought scapegoats for the disaster. Ready to hand were prisoners who had escaped when the prison walls collapsed. Blamed for the outbreak of fire and for looting, hundreds of them were rounded up and publicly hanged. Heretics were also blamed, and the priests of the Inquisition set up a hunt for

Below: The Inquisition executing heretics.

those whose guilt must have brought about the calamity. Only after the first hysteria had died down was attention turned to tending the survivors and rebuilding the city; then, the counsel of secretary of state the Marquis de Pombal was heeded: 'We must bury the dead and feed the living.'

The shock was to have a lasting impact on the Age of Reason and inspired the French philosopher Voltaire to write his most famous book *Candide* (1759), in which he satirized the optimistic belief that Man lived in 'the best of all possible worlds'.

Below: Modern buildings are often unable to withstand the terrible forces exerted by earthquakes, just as those in Lisbon buckled and crumbled on 1 November 1755.

GLASNOST SAVES LIVES

Had it not been for Soviet President Mikhail Gorbachev's then recently declared policy of *Glasnost* ('Openness'), the West might have heard little of one of the greatest tragedies of recent years, the Armenian earthquake of 7 December 1988. A massive shock affected a densely populated area extending over some 10,400sq km (4,000sq mi), almost completely destroying the three cities of Leninakan, Kirovakan and Spitak. For the first time, the USSR admitted its incapacity to cope alone, and accepted aid from all countries (67, including the USA) that offered it. Even so, the official death toll was put at around 25,000.

21

THE SAN FRANCISCO EARTHQUAKES

ALONG MOST of the length of California stretches the San Andreas Fault: a mighty fracture in the Earth's crust, along which the land masses on either side slide slowly past one another. Sometimes, however, the Pacific plate and the North American plate jam against each other; then pressure builds up until they break free in a monstrous earthquake.

The city of San Francisco grew up in the 1840s as a major commercial and cultural centre: 'the American Paris'. But the city was built on something even more shifting than sand: it was built right by the San Andreas Fault. On 18 April 1906, the people of San Francisco learned just how vulnerable their position was when a massive earthquake, followed by raging fire, all but obliterated the city, destroying 28,188 buildings and killing some 700 people.

The first shock hit in the small hours of the morning. Blasting from its start point 145km (90mi) north of San Francisco at 3.2km/sec (2mi/sec), it toppled large buildings in seconds and ripped open huge cracks in the ground which swallowed people and vehicles – then slammed shut upon them. One survivor reported: 'The street seemed to move like waves of water'; another described buildings moving 'in what looked like a crazy dance' then 'crumbling as one might crush a biscuit in one's hand'. Masonry crashed down into the street, and church spires fell like spears. Wood-frame buildings all along the coastal strip collapsed into a 4.5m (15ft)-high mess of broken houses, dead men and horses.

PILLARS OF SMOKE

Within half an hour came the fire, which ignited in more than 50 places at once from toppled stoves, ruptured gas mains and broken electric wires, and spread across the city. By the next day, ships 160km (100mi) out at sea could see the pillars of smoke rising into the sky. San Francisco's fire chief had planned, in such a contingency, to use dynamite to blast fire-breaks and halt the flames, but he was killed in the quake's first moments, and unskilled troops laying

Left: The City Hall, San Francisco, was destroyed by an earthquake in April 1906. Above: The Agassiz statue at Stanford, Santa Clara County, was also damaged.

dynamite charges without supervision unwittingly started more fires than they put out. Half the city went up in flames, while survivors fled by boat or rail or climbed to higher ground. At last the fire was defeated. On the waterfront, fire crews were able to pump water from the bay; farther inland, dynamiters blew up the city's widest street to create a 53m (175ft)-wide corridor between the flames and the western side of the city.

For three days mayhem reigned in the shattered, burning city. Homeless, hungry, panic-stricken survivors crowded the streets. Among them moved a steady stream of looters – while troops and vigilante groups fought back with firing squads and makeshift gallows to execute lawbreakers (and some innocent people fleeing the devastation) on the spot. The human refugees were joined by thousands of rats, driven out by the fire from their underground homes – many of them carrying deadly bubonic plague. Within a year more than 150 cases of rat-spread plague had been reported.

The city rose again like a phoenix; but the San Andreas Fault remained with all its potential for disaster. On 17 October 1989, a 40km (25mi) stretch of the Fault 'lurched', causing an earthquake in the Santa Cruz mountains some 100km (62mi) southeast of San Francisco. It was the third largest earthquake to hit the USA since the horror of 1906. Although only 62 people were killed, more than 3,000 were injured and nearly 19,000 left homeless. Roads and viaducts for miles around were shattered. The worst damage occurred on the northern shore of San Francisco, where fires and gas explosions added to the dangers.

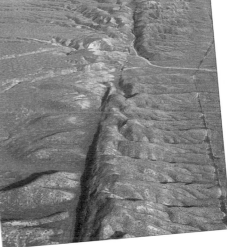

Top: A collapsed section of the Cypress viaduct of Interstate 880, California, after the Loma Prieta earthquake, 1989.
Above: The San Andreas Fault.

ITALIAN IMPROVIZATION

Water mains in the area had ruptured; but during the 1906 earthquake the resourceful Italian community on San Francisco's Telegraph Hill managed to halt the blaze in their area by pouring some 4,550 litres (1,000 gallons) of wine onto the flames. Italy's then most famous son, the great operatic tenor Enrico Caruso, was among the survivors of the quake; he was quoted as saying that it was 'like an eruption of Vesuvius'.

THE DAY THE EARTH SIGHED

JAPAN, SITUATED on the Pacific 'Ring of Fire' (the great band of seismic activity running around the Pacific rim from New Zealand to Cape Horn), is well used to earthquakes. There was no warning that the earthquake that struck the Kanto Plain at noon on 1 September 1923 would be the nation's most destructive horror until World War II. In Tokyo, the capital, and in the major seaport of Yokohama about 29km (18mi) away, folk were peacefully cooking their midday meals. Then, some 80km (50mi) south of Tokyo, the quake ripped open the seabed beneath Sagami Bay, sending violent tremors across the land and raising massive tsunami along the coast.

In Tokyo, said a survivor later, 'The ground rose as though Earth was heaving a sigh.' Buildings swayed, crumpled and fell. Although some people were killed by falling masonry, many of Tokyo's dwellings were lightly constructed as a specific precaution against earthquakes, and collapsed without severe harm to their occupants. People sought safety in open spaces – but found none. From thousands of open braziers where food had been cooking, fire spilled onto the wood, fabric and paper of the ruined houses. Strong winds fanned the flames, and in minutes much of Tokyo was ablaze. The city's narrow streets and bridges proved deathtraps where the fleeing refugees found themselves caught between advancing walls of flame.

A VIOLENT FIRESTORM

Police and firemen directed survivors to areas thought to be of greater safety, including a park on the east bank of the Sumida River. In this assembly area, some 40,000 people were packed tightly together by mid-afternoon – only to be struck by a violent firestorm which killed more than 30,000 almost instantaneously. Crowds who had fled to the rivers or to the great moat surrounding the Imperial Palace were burned, asphyxiated, even boiled alive, as they stood up to their necks in water; others were drowned or crushed when bridges collapsed under the weight of the crowds stampeding to supposed safety.

The seaport of Yokohama was equally hard hit. The first shock sent a hospital, with all its occupants, and many homes crashing from the heights above the port. In the bay, the major pier, where the liner *Empress of Australia* was loading, rose into the air 'like a giant caterpillar'. Oil tanks at the naval dockyard ruptured, and soon the bay was covered with burning oil, in which hundreds of people swept from the quays and promenade were cremated. *The Empress of Australia*, towed out of danger by a tug and a Dutch oil tanker (the latter fully loaded!), picked up some 12,000 persons from the

water or from small boats. Even so, 21,000 died in Yokohama, where 60,000 buildings (about 80 per cent of the port) were destroyed. Elsewhere along the coast, hundreds of people were swept away by tidal waves or buried by landslides.

The overall death toll is estimated at 150,000 dead or missing and 100,000 seriously injured. In Tokyo, more than 300,000 buildings were destroyed and some 1,500,000 persons made homeless. The government, with generous foreign aid, notably from the USA, acted swiftly to restore order and services – but not before a number of Koreans (unpopular underlings in the then rigid Japanese class society) had been lynched by people who blamed them for the violent crime and looting that immediately followed the catastrophe.

Below and right: Scenes of the tremendous devastation caused by earthquake and fire in Tokyo on 1 September 1923.

ARCHITECT OF SAFETY

Almost all of Tokyo's major buildings – including the great Imperial University Library, 5,000 banks, 2,500 places of worship, and 20,000 factories and warehouses – were destroyed by earthquake or fire. Of the few to survive, the largest (and newest) was the Imperial Hotel, completed in 1922 to the design of the controversial American architect Frank Lloyd Wright (1869–1959). His many critics had predicted that the first tremor would bring down the steel and masonry building – but Wright's use of what he termed 'floating cantilever construction' enabled it to ride out the quake virtually undamaged.

25

ALASKA'S GREAT UPHEAVALS

ONE OF the world's most active seismic zones lies beneath Alaska, and during this century alone, close on 80 major quakes have struck southern Alaska and the nearby Aleutian Islands. The results of one powerful upheaval may be viewed today in the magnificent Katmai National Park. Here, in 1912, a new volcano, Novarupta, burst into being, while neighbouring Mount Katmai collapsed.

Quakes shook the ground over a three-day period, during which the mountains hurled aloft vast amounts of volcanic debris, darkening the skies for 160km (100mi) around and covering an area of 108,800sq km (42,000sq mi) with ash.

Another dramatic quake hit Alaska in 1958, in the Yakutat Bay area. Coastal cliffs came crashing down, while the quake set off a gigantic landslide (estimated volume 30,584,000cu m/40,000,000cu yd). This tumbled into the sea at Lituya Bay with such force that it sent a wave splashing to a height of 530m (1,740ft) on a mountainside. The great mass of water surged violently back and forth across the bay until 10sq km(4sq mi) of forest along its shores was ripped out and the mountain was stripped down to bedrock. As the quake struck, fishermen out in the bay watched while 'a whole mountain came down' and their boats leapt out of the water, to be swept, miraculously, to safety.

The big one hit Alaska on 27 March 1964. It was the USA's largest recorded earthquake, shaking an area of 80,000sq km (31,000sq mi). Mountains and islands were moved; a chunk of sea-bed 440km (275mi) across, lying between Kodiak and Montague Islands, was raised 15m (50ft) above sea level, and land and sea-bed levels were altered over an area of 160,000sq km (62,000sq mi).

EARTH TREMORS

This mighty upheaval began early in the evening, when a great rumbling was followed by earth tremors lasting four minutes. The settlements of southern Alaska, including Anchorage, the state's largest town, are built on water-laden glacial silt; this was liquefied by the vibrations, so that the ground gave way beneath buildings. In a live radio broadcast from Anchorage, listeners were told: 'the whole place just moved like somebody had taken it by the nape of the neck and was shaking it…this house was shaking like a leaf… and it's still swaying back and forth…' Buildings were shaken to pieces; fissures in the ground swallowed some; landslides carried others away. Roads, bridges, railways cracked, subsided or rose; harbours were lifted out of the water; Alaska's entire communications system was plunged into chaos.

At the port of Valdez, landslides swept the quayside (and 30 people waiting for a boat) into the sea, fire broke out among oil-storage tanks ruptured by the quake, and tsunamis smashed the waterfront. The town was so badly damaged that it later had to be rebuilt on a new site. Tsunamis marched along the coast and

All pictures: Earthquake damage to roads, bridges and railways in Alaska.

swept down the Canadian and American seaboard as far as northern California. In the north, they destroyed half the Kodiak Island fishing fleet, smashing 77 boats; to the south, they drowned people as far away as Oregon and California.

Mercifully, the death toll was low (131 persons, of whom 122 were killed by tsunamis in Alaska, British Columbia, Oregon and California), even considering the small population of Alaska. But if ever an earthquake could be considered well-timed, it was this one: in March, the tourist season had not yet begun, fish canneries had not opened for the season, and because winter weather was past, earthquake victims did not die of exposure. Even the time of day was well chosen: schools and offices had already closed, and it was low tide, reducing the impact of the tsunamis. But property losses were catastrophic: the disaster ruined three-quarters of Alaska's trade and industry and left thousands homeless.

THE PLAGUE FROM UNDERGROUND

Fire and flood are the usual killers that accompany earthquakes. In the aftermath of the severe quake and tsunami that devastated the Mediterranean port of Agadir, Morocco, on 29 February 1960, toppling 70 per cent of its buildings and killing some 12,000 persons, another terror threatened – plague. The danger came in the form of tens of thousands of rats, driven above-ground when the city's sewers burst. French and American military personnel, the first helpers on the scene, made destruction of these potentially deadly vermin a priority.

THE HOUR (OR MINUTE) OF DOOM

ISLAM TEACHES that the world will end with a mighty earthquake: 'the earthquake of the Hour of Doom'. In northern Iran, on 22 June 1990, many must have believed that the hour (or minute) of doom had come as their world fell to pieces. The quake which hit the farming provinces of Zanjan and Gilan, near the Russian border, was even more catastrophic than the destructive shocks of 1968 and 1978, which killed 18,000 and 25,000 persons respectively. Measuring 7.7 on the Richter Scale, the 1990 quake ravaged 260sq km (100sq mi) in 60 seconds.

Scores of towns were levelled, burying people under the wreckage of their homes, and leaving some 400,000 survivors without shelter. At least 45,000 people died immediately; the rest, including about 100,000 injured, endured a further 36 hours of aftershocks. Villages which survived the quake were cut off from supplies. In the face of such devastation, and after three days' national mourning, Iran's anti-Western foreign policy gave way to acceptance of much-needed aid.

CALIFORNIAN NIGHTMARE

Four years later, Iran's 'bogeyman' suffered when a quake hit Los Angeles, California. For many years, Angelenos had feared that the next shift of the San Andreas Fault, only 48km (30mi) away, might shatter their city. On 17 January 1994, it seemed the time had come. In the suburb of Northridge, the ground lurched violently, toppling apartment blocks and ripping up roads and bridges. Ruptured power lines plunged more than

28

Above: Support columns of a bridge protrude through the road bed in California, following the Loma Prieta earthquake in 1989.

Above: This house dropped from its foundations to lean against its neighbour following the severe earthquake in San Francisco, California, in 1906.

*Above: Damage to Olive View Hospital,
after the San Fernando earthquake, 1971.
Right: Aerial view of the San Andreas Fault.*

THE SAN ANDREAS FAULT

The San Andreas Fault, running along the Pacific coast north of San Francisco and southeast into Mexico, is remarkable not only for its great length, but in that, unlike most faults, it is not merely a break in a single rock formation but a division between the American and the Pacific tectonic plates, which grind slowly but steadily past each other at an average rate of 1cm (0.4in) a year, causing massive pressure to build up when they jam. Because some sections of the fault have been stationary for years, scientists predict a 'Big One' along the Fault within 50 years.

29

3,000,000 citizens into darkness; shattered gas lines and oil mains fuelled fires – some extinguished by floods from broken water mains. More than 1,000 aftershocks hampered rescue work, and 58 people died.

Despite damage estimated at up to $30 billion, it wasn't the dreaded 'Big One'. The San Andreas Fault, an 1,290km (800mi) crack in Earth's crust stretching through California, has the potential to produce a quake 85 times more powerful than the 1994 shock (which registered 6.6 on the Richter Scale). But this quake was fathered by one of many smaller cracks criss-crossing California – a hitherto unsuspected rift some 14.5km (9mi) beneath Northridge. 'The Big One' may yet come, but LA (which claims its four seasons are riots, earthquakes, fire and floods) seems ill-prepared: despite a civic resolution made after the 1971 quake to strengthen freeway bridges and other structures, work had not been completed by 1994.

MEASURING EARTHQUAKES

Earthquakes range in intensity from slight tremors (some 100,000 per year) to catastrophic upheavals. In 1935, American seismologist Charles Richter (1900–1985) devised a mathematical formula to measure earthquake magnitude. The Richter Scale, now used worldwide, runs logarithmically from 0 to 10, each unit representing a tenfold increase in the intensity of earthquake waves. Magnitude does not necessarily indicate intensity, or reflect impact on human lives: the earthquake at Agadir, Morocco, in 1960, magnitude 5.8, killed 140 times more people than the Anchorage earthquake (pages 26-27) of magnitude 8.4. Intensity is measured by observation of the earthquake's effect, using a scale based on that devised by the Italian geologist Giuseppe Mercalli (1815–1914) in 1902. On the modified Mercalli Scale, intensity runs from 1 (barely felt) to 12 (major ground disturbance and catastrophic damage).

FIRE DOWN BELOW: VOLCANOES

I N ANCIENT times, when our ancestors saw burning rock bursting out of the ground they recognized it as the fire of the gods. Beneath the ground, they believed, the smith god kept his furnace blazing, and sometimes stoked it too fiercely. Today, we still call these eruptions volcanoes, after the forge of Roman god Vulcan.

Far beneath the calm surface of our planet, near the Earth's red-hot core, molten rock (magma) seethes like boiling porridge. Over most of the world's surface, the Earth's crust forms a secure lid to prevent the magma escaping. But where it finds a crack or a weak spot, the molten rock forces its way upwards and bursts out as lava in a volcanic eruption. Often the lava gushes out in fountains, to flow for some distance before gradually solidifying in contact with the cool air. Along with ash and other detritus, it may build up around its exit point into the characteristic conical hill which forms the popular image of a volcano.

VOLCANIC ERUPTION

Not all volcanoes behave in the same way. Much depends on the silica content of the magma itself. A low silica content (under 55 per cent) produces a free-flowing basic magma which is very hot (c.1,200°C/2,192°F) and from which gases usually escape quite easily. This creates the type of volcanic eruption we see in children's cartoons, with lava gushing out as freely as water from a burst pipe. With a higher silica content (55-70 per cent), the magma is thicker and also cooler (700-900°C/1,292-1,652°F). Gases which escape freely from basic magma are trapped within the viscous silicic magma, building up until

they burst out in huge explosions which shatter the lava into dust or fine ash.

Some volcanoes are on the simmer the whole time, like the one that gives its name to the Mediterranean island of Stromboli, in the Tyrrhenian Sea off northeast Sicily. Stromboli produces minor eruptions on most days. Some volcanoes lie dormant for decades, even centuries, between eruptions; some have exhausted their fury and are dead. The lava flow is only the most spectacular and immediately threatening result of an eruption: further effects include tsunamis

BURIED IN THE MUD

One of the deadliest volcanic eruptions of all time occurred in November 1985, when 23,000 people died in a sea of mud after the eruption of the long-dormant volcano of Nevado del Ruiz, Colombia. There was no spectacular lava display; instead, the eruption melted one-tenth of the volcano's ice-cap, triggering off torrents of mud, rocks, ashes and other debris. A major mud-flow rushed down the valley of the River Azufrado, where a wall of mud 30m (98ft) high, travelling at 36km/h (22mph), destroyed the town of Armero. Of 5,000 houses, only 100 were left standing – and only the town's cemetery remained untouched. One survivor, Rosa Maria Henao, said the wave 'rolled into town with a moaning sound, like some sort of monster.' She and her children climbed to the roof of their hilltop home and watched the town engulfed: 'It seemed like the end of the world!'

(tidal waves; see pages 46-47 *et seq*), mud-flows, or flooding caused by melted ice. The gas and ash spewed out may kill crops and animals, contributing to famine. Ash and gas in the atmosphere also affect air quality, causing respiratory ailments. Major eruptions affect the whole global climate – both the end of the dinosaurs 65 million years ago (see pages 10-11) and the onset of the Ice Age 10,000 years ago may have owed much to the impact of volcanic eruptions on the atmosphere

Estimates of the number of active volcanoes today vary widely – since it is not always certain whether a long-dormant volcano is dead or alive – between 700 and 1,500.

All pictures: When the molten rock near the Earth's red-hot core finds a weakness in our planet's crust, it pours forth as volcanic eruptions of flaming magma, lava flows and clouds of dust and ash. People are powerless to counter the devastating effects of these explosions on their property.

IS 'THE EXPLOSIVE CENTURY' COMING?

In 1997 a study group of British scientists led by Professor Bill McGuire of University College, London, predicted that the 21st century might be 'the century of the volcano...one of the most explosive on record'. They discovered that in the past rises in sea levels caused by global warming have usually been followed by surges in volcanic activity. Among the possible effects of present-day global warming is the melting of huge sections of the polar icecaps. Ninety per cent of Earth's volcanoes are close to or surrounded by sea; if rising water erodes and weakens their rocky sides, they will become unable to withstand the internal pressure of molten rock and will erupt. Europe has seen a recent surge in volcanic activity: a volcano near Rome, dormant for 20,000 years, is waking; a huge volcano is growing from sea bed just north of Crete.

31

DROWNED ATLANTIS

ONE OF the favourite mysteries of modern chroniclers of the unexplained is the lost land of Atlantis. Some 2,400 years ago, the Greek philosopher Plato wrote of this mysterious island, peopled by a highly advanced society, which sank beneath the waves in a single night. Ever since, scholars have debated whether he invented Atlantis, or was recording a genuine tradition.

Seekers after the drowned land have pursued their investigations in places as widely separated as Sweden, Palestine, Central Asia, North Africa, Mexico, Cornwall, Spain, Nigeria, and Bolivia! However, the most likely candidate for a historical Atlantis, if we take the view that Plato's account – in which he describes 'violent earthquakes and floods', caused by the wrath of Zeus, the father god, before the island 'disappeared in the depths of the sea' – was based on folk memories of an event long before his time, is the Greek island of Thera (Thira), known from the Middle Ages until the 19th century as Santorini, in the southern Aegean.

Modern Thera is crescent-shaped, about 19km (12mi) long and 5km (3mi) wide. It was once much larger, for what remains today is only a part of a huge volcanic crater. Around the year 1628 BC (according to recent carbon-dating), the peaceful Bronze Age community on Thera was racked by earthquakes which badly damaged the large, prosperous city, with its busy harbour and fine, multi-storeyed dwellings decorated with sophisticated wall paintings. Reconstruction quickly began, but then a new disaster was threatened in the form of the island's volcano, called Stronghyle ('The Round One'). The signs of eruption must have come both suddenly and unmistakably, for archaeological evidence shows that repair work was abruptly abandoned; workmen threw aside their gear, leaving bowls of plaster near newly rebuilt walls. People simply grabbed their portable valuables and evacuated the island.

We know, from the absence of human remains in the buried town, that they

Above and opposite top: Eruptions of the submarine volcano at Santorini, Bay of Thera, in the Greek Archipelago.

32

escaped just in time, before an explosion lifted the top from the volcano. Their city was buried beneath metres of pumice. In the aftermath of the detonation, the volcano's main cone collapsed and the sea poured into the crater. All that remained of the original island of Thera was three fragments: the modern Thera and the smaller islands of Therasia and Aspronisi. What was once the centre of the island was now underwater.

Elsewhere, the eruption left an area of some 200,000sq km (77,200sq mi) covered with volcanic ash; noxious gas and darkened skies must have affected the surrounding lands for many weeks. The effects of Thera's destruction throughout the Mediterranean lands have been seized on at various times by historians to explain such phenomena as the plague of darkness that assisted the Israelites to leave Egypt (see pages 8-9), the subsequent parting of the Red Sea in their path, and even the disappearance of the Minoan civilization of Crete.

THE SEA BOILED AND BLAZED

A few centuries after the eruption, people returned and built new homes on ash-covered sites. But the volcano remained a threatening presence. In 197 BC an eruption pushed up a new islet (today known as Palaea Kameni) in Thera's bay; the Greek historian Strabo described how 'between Thera and Therasia fires broke forth from the sea, and continued for four days, so that the whole sea boiled and blazed, and the fires cast up an island, which was gradually elevated as though by levers, and consisted of burning masses.' Upheavals continued into modern times: between 1866 and 1950 five periods of volcanic activity created a new island, Nea Kameni.

The original disaster was forgotten until the 1860s–70s, when workmen quarrying pumice on Thera for use in building the Suez Canal uncovered extensive Bronze Age remains, including walls painted with magnificent frescoes and finely decorated vases. Recently, archaeologists have uncovered much more of the buried town.

FALL OF THE MINOAN EMPIRE

In the 1930s, the Greek archaeologist Spyridon Marinatos concluded that Thera's eruption was the cause of the mysterious downfall of the great Minoan empire of Crete. This theory, still to be found in some reference books, is now rejected by most archaeologists, since carbon-dating suggests that the Minoan empire was destroyed by invaders from the Greek mainland, not natural disasters. However, the eruption on Thera and subsequent earthquakes on Crete may have weakened Minoan power.

BURIED CITIES

MOUNT VESUVIUS (1,186m/3,891ft), near the Bay of Naples in southern Italy, is one of the world's most famous active volcanoes. Two thousand years ago, it was not so well known. The Romans, believing it to be extinct and harmless, developed the great city of Naples and built several other large towns in its shadow. Then, in AD 79, the volcano came to life with a vengeance. On 24-27 August, a violent eruption laid waste the surrounding province.

This eruption has gone down as one of the worst in recorded history, claiming 16,000-20,000 lives. It is also notable as the earliest eruption for which a detailed contemporary account has survived, and as the tomb in which two Roman towns were preserved in almost mint condition, offering modern generations a window on everyday life in Roman times.

Vesuvius blasted off with a monstrous column of gas, steam, ash and pumice rising high into the sky. The Roman historian Pliny the Younger described it as a tree-shaped cloud, which 'rose up high in a kind of trunk and then divided into branches.' Ash and dust poured down onto the countryside, blackening the land. At least six times, the towering column collapsed in a fiery mass which came streaming down the volcano's sides, destroying everything that lay in its path. Many were caught in the burning streams; others suffocated in the fumes. The cities of Pompeii, Herculaneum and Stabiae were completely destroyed.

Pompeii was buried, with some 2,000 of its c.15,000 inhabitants, under 4m (13ft) of molten lava, to lie forgotten for centuries. When excavation began in the 18th century, archaeologists were amazed at the wealth of material. The citizens had fled for their lives in such haste that they left meals on their tables, loaves baking in their ovens, and unfinished drinks on bar counters. More than half the city has now been uncovered, revealing not only the straight, stone-paved streets, fine public buildings and comfortable villas that we associate with the Romans, but the less familiar tenement rooms of the poor, and the shops, taverns, and factories of a busy trading centre. The lava preserved even the tragic remains of those who did not escape: ash and pumice encased their bodies to form casts. Families lie together where they fell; one man died struggling to rescue an obstinate goat; among the ruins lies a much-loved dog whose collar bears an inscription telling us that he twice saved his owner's life.

BURIED UNDER BOILING MUD

The small provincial town of Herculaneum was buried under 15-20m (50-65ft) of boiling mud. It was to achieve in its death an importance it had not enjoyed while it lived. The mud, unlike the hot ashes that covered Pompeii, carbonized and preserved fragile materials like wood, cloth, and even rolls of papyrus. Home furnishings such as beds, tables, a household shrine

Above: Mount Etna is Europe's highest active volcano, and erupts with alarming regularity.

MOUNT ETNA RUMBLES ON

Above: Vesuvius, near the Bay of Naples, is one of the world's most famous volcanoes. Left: Eruption of Mount Etna, Sicily, 1910.

Europe's highest active volcano, Mount Etna (3,263m/10,705ft) stands on the eastern coast of Sicily. It has been active for about 2,000,000 years, and more than 250 eruptions have been historically recorded. Among the most violent were those of 475 BC; of AD 1169, when the town of Catania was destroyed with 15,000 of its inhabitants; and of 1669, when more than 20,000 were killed. In 1928 two villages were buried by a flow of lava. More recent eruptions have occurred in 1971, 1979, 1983 and 1992.

and a baby's cot with rockers survive to give us a picture of Herculaneum's everyday life .

Since this outbreak, Vesuvius has remained a constant threat. There were about 10 minor eruptions over the next 1,500 years. The next major blast occurred in December 1631, when lava and mudflows poured down upon Naples and the surrounding towns, causing a death toll estimated as high as 18,000. The volcano exploded again in 1794, 1872 and 1906; the last major eruption was in 1944. Today its activity is carefully monitored.

BIG BANG: KRAKATOA

ON 27 AUGUST 1883, the Indonesian island of Krakatoa (Krakatau) blew up with the biggest bang in recorded history: an explosion heard 4,800km (3,000mi) away. After two centuries of inactivity, the small volcanic island, lying between Java and Sumatra in the Sunda Strait, had begun to simmer in May; now, the volcano blew its top in four gigantic explosions (the third being the big bang).

The first warning of the horror to come was revealed by a series of small explosions on 20 May 1883. Tourists observed 'a vast column of steam issuing with a terrific noise' from a fissure near the crater. On 11 August, a survey team landed on the island and found that it lay beneath a covering of some 50cm (20in) of volcanic dust, while steam spurted from several sites. On 26 August, dwellers on nearby islands were awakened by the first major explosion. The captain of a ship 65km (40mi) away reported: 'Krakatoa was a terrifying glory…an immense wall, with bursts of forked lightning darting through it.'

DARKNESS RULED THE SKIES

Intermittent explosions continued until, next day, a giant detonation blew the cone of Krakatoa to fragments. The explosion was heard in Australia and the USA. Pieces of rock up to 2m (7ft) in width were hurled across an area larger than France. Such a vast amount of volcanic debris – ash, dust and pumice – was blasted 80km (50mi) upwards into the atmosphere, that the darkness of night ruled the skies over an area some 450km (280mi) in circumference. In areas up to 210km (130mi) away, this darkness endured for 22 hours. This enormous dust cloud travelled around the Earth, causing brilliant red sunsets worldwide for three years afterwards.

In the immediate area of the big bang, the collapsing volcanic cone turned the sea into a raging maelstrom, swallowing up coastal shipping. Within 30 minutes of the detonation, seismic tidal waves up to 30m (100ft) high were racing from the site to break on the coasts of Java and Sumatra, where they destroyed or severely damaged 295 towns. Even the English Channel, halfway around the world, experienced giant waves and very high tides. Krakatoa's detonation signalled a burst of activity from other volcanoes throughout Java, during which sizable areas of the Malay Archipelago

and coastal Java sank beneath the sea, islands disappeared, and new volcanic peaks thrust up from beneath the sea.

ENORMOUS DEATH TOLL

Although Krakatoa itself was uninhabited, the death toll was enormous: fire, molten lava, and rains of ash and rocks killed many persons; tidal waves killed more. At least 36,000 people died; some reports put the death toll as high as 200,000. The explosion destroyed some two-thirds of Krakatoa island, which today is roughly circular and about 5km (3mi) in diameter, dominated by the 810m (2,650ft) peak of the still-active volcano. In the aftermath, the remains of the island, once luxuriantly forested, were a barren waste: the first life, a spider, was recorded five months later, and by the 1920s the jungle had returned. Further volcanic eruptions on the seabed began to produce a new island, Anak Krakatau ('Child of Krakatoa'), which rose above sea level in 1928. It has erupted at regular intervals ever since, and it is estimated that in 600 years it will be as big as its parent originally was – and perhaps as deadly.

Left: A view of Krakatoa during the early stages of eruption in 1883. On 27 August the Indonesian island exploded with the biggest bang in recorded history.
Right: A sudden volcanic eruption in Java.

DISASTER MOVIE

Hollywood caught a cold with the disaster movie *Krakatoa, East of Java*, released in 1969. Critics not only panned the costly spectacular – but also gleefully pointed out that Krakatoa is, in fact, *west* of Java.

THE YEAR WITHOUT A SUMMER

Indonesia suffers more volcanic destruction than any other region – at least 76 volcanoes have erupted in its archipelago in historic times. One of the worst was on 10 April 1815, when the 3,960m (13,000ft) peak of Tambora, on Sumbawa island, blew up. It sank Sumbawa into the ocean, and covered neighbouring islands more than 1m (3ft) deep in ash. As many as 90,000 may have died, either in the blast or in subsequent tidal waves, famine and cholera outbreak among starving survivors. An estimated 1,700,000 tonnes of debris was thrown into the sky, causing a three-day 'night' for 650km (400mi) around. Its effect on the atmosphere caused 1815 to be known across the world as 'the year without a summer' or, in New England, as 'Eighteen hundred and froze to death'.

CARNAGE IN THE CARIBBEAN

LIVING ON a volcanic island is dicing with death, even when the volcano has been long dormant. One of the deadliest eruptions of modern times occurred on the island of Martinique in the West Indies in 1902. Mont Pelée had shown little activity for some 300 years, and the town of St. Pierre, 'pearl of the West Indies', below it was prosperous.

Warning signs began in April 1902: a sulphuric smell, minor eruptions, a rain of ash. Ants, centipedes and snakes, fleeing their mountain homes, invaded the streets – and 50 humans and 200 animals died of snakebite in a single afternoon. There was a steady increase in explosive eruptions; one triggered an avalanche of mud which buried a sugar mill and its 150 workers. There were calls for the evacuation of St. Pierre's 30,000 inhabitants, but a Scientific Commission said there was no danger.

So, on 8 May, St. Pierre was still fully inhabited when the volcano burst apart, showering it with molten lava, ash, and gas, and wiping out almost all its people and buildings. Ships in the harbour were wrecked: one of the few survivors of the crew of the steamship *Roraima* told how 'The side of the volcano was ripped out, and there hurled straight towards us a solid wall of flame [which] sounded like a thousand cannon…The town vanished before our eyes.' Estimates of the death toll range from 28,000 to 40,000. One of only 70 survivors in the city was a gaol-bird who was trapped, but also protected, in a stone cell, from which he was rescued, scorched but alive, some days later.

STEAM-BLAST ERUPTIONS

This devastating type of eruption now takes its name from Mont Pelée. A Peléan eruption is characterized by the

Island fauna often develop into unique species, but their limited range makes them very vulnerable – and a volcanic eruption can wipe out most of an island species. Mount Pelée's 1902 eruption caused havoc to local wildlife, and destroyed the entire population of a little rodent which lived only on its slopes, the Martinique Muskrat or Pilori. The 1997 eruption of the Soufriere Hills volcano may yet cause another extinction: Montserrat's national bird, the Montserrat Oriole, one of the world's rarest species and found nowhere else. Fewer than 200 survived the eruption, and, with much of the birds' habitat destroyed, the island's government is seeking preservation measures.

39

Left: Many areas of Central America and the Caribbean suffer from seismic activity. This picture portrays an earthquake and volcanic eruption in El Salvador in 1937.

detonation of a long-dormant volcano with little warning, with steam-blast eruptions tearing the cone apart and showering fragments up to 10km (6.5 mi). Viscous silicic lava produces violent gas explosions, and *nuées ardentes* (glowing, steam-powered avalanches of gas and burning ash) incinerate everything in their path.

Only a few hours before the catastrophe on Martinique, about 145km (90mi) to the south, another West Indian volcano had exploded: La Soufriere, a 1,230m (4,035ft) high peak on the island of St. Vincent. Preliminary earthquakes had provided sufficient warning for some

of the population to evacuate, but 1,565 persons died under a hail of red-hot stones and ash and in mud-flows.

DISASTER IN THE CARIBBEAN

A more recent volcanic disaster in the Caribbean struck the small island of Montserrat (110sq km/42sq mi), which had been devastated by Hurricane Hugo in 1989. In July 1997, the Soufriere Hills volcano, dormant for 400 years, erupted. It has been spewing out rock and ash ever since: the southern half of island is covered with it; the capital city, Plymouth, is half-buried. A tropical

paradise has become a barren wasteland, as rain mixes with dust and ash to form a sticky layer like wet cement. Thousands had to be evacuated from their homes (the last occupant of Plymouth was a 12-week-old puppy, now called Plymouth and living in Massachusetts), and rescuers worked in streets up to 2.4m (8ft) deep in hot ash. The World Society for Protection of Animals sent emergency aid teams to rescue hundreds of feral animals (dogs, pigs, goats, cattle, donkeys and agoutis) from danger areas and transport them to specially built animal shelters; more than 200 rescued pets were airlifted to Florida.

FIRE AND ICE

ICELAND IS a land of extremes: ice and fire. The large island (103,000sq km/39,770sq mi) is a volcanic creation, formed by a series of volcanoes lying along one of the weakest spots in the Earth's crust, a major fault line called the Mid-Atlantic Ridge. Iceland's volcanic heights are capped with snowfields and vast glaciers, the largest of which – Vatnajökull; more than 145km (90mi) long and 95km (60mi) across – covers an area equal to that of all continental Europe's glaciers put together.

Yet many areas are able to grow tropical plants such as bananas, because Iceland's constant volcanic activity supplies it with hot springs, geothermal energy from which is used to heat huge greenhouses, as well as homes in many towns. In addition to hot water, underground volcanic activity produces towering geysers, vents spraying out hot gases, and lakes of boiling mud.

Iceland has more than 200 volcanoes, 30 of which have erupted in modern times. The island's worst volcanic disaster since its settlement in AD 875 occurred in the summer of 1783, at Laki volcanic ridge. Throughout May, a series of ground tremors and a steaming, bubbling sea filled Icelanders with alarm. In June, Laki mountain burst open with a roar, tearing open a 24km (15mi) fissure from which poured the largest lava flow in recorded history. A river of lava up to 80km(50mi) long and 30m (100ft) deep flowed inexorably across the land, engulfing villages on its way. Molten rock fountained 1km (0.62mi) into the air; gas explosions hurled ash and dust to a height of 12km (7.5mi). The eruptions continued until February 1784, by which time the lava covered an area of some 600sq km (230sq mi).

Above: Fire and ice form a deadly combination when a glacier-capped volcano erupts, producing great floods of meltwater.

ENCROACHING LAVA

Farmers and villagers grabbed their belongings and fled before the encroaching lava. It seemed they had escaped with their lives – but worse was to come. Ash covered much of Iceland's pastures, while volcanic gases poisoned the air, killing two-thirds of the country's cattle, horses and sheep as well as much of the coastal fish stocks. One-quarter of Iceland's population died in the ensuing famine over the next three years; the toxic chemicals poisoning farmland inflicted diseases and deformities upon those who survived. An eye-watering blue haze hung over the land, killing Iceland's trees, grass and crops, scorching plant life across much of Europe, and cutting off the Sun's heat to bring the bitterest winters for 250 years as far away as the USA.

Above and below: Iceland experiences constant seismic activity which manifests itself in volcanic eruptions and hot geysers.

GLACIER-BURST

Fire and ice form a deadly combination when a glacier-capped volcano erupts, producing great floods of meltwater. When Iceland's highest mountain, Öræfajökull (2,119m/6,952 feet), erupted in 1362, torrents of melted ice swept 40 farms, with all their occupants and livestock, into the sea. The huge glacier of Vatnajökull lies directly over a large volcanic fissure. When this erupts, the lower strata of ice melt to form a lake beneath the ice-cap. This grows until water pressure forces up the restraining lid of ice (which may be up to 500m/1,640ft thick); then a torrent comes roaring down the mountain-side. A glacier-burst in 1934 produced more than 15cu km (3.5cu mi) of flood water.

BIRTH OF AN ISLAND

In November 1963 smoke began pouring from the sea near the Vestmann Islands, off Iceland's south coast. It signalled the start of a violent underwater volcanic eruption. Soon columns of ash and steam were blasted 400m (1,300ft) above the sea, and within a few hours a cone of lava thrust up to form a new island, now called Surtsey, after the fire-giant Surtr of Viking legend. Over the next few months the volcano and the Atlantic Ocean battled over Surtsey, the one building it up, the other breaking it down. Two other small islets thrown up over the next two years succumbed to oceanic erosion, but Surtsey remains. Within months of its appearance, plants had begun to colonize the new land.

SPITTING THUNDER EGGS

UNTIL 1980, no volcano in the USA had caused a human death within recorded history. In 1975, geologists warned that the dormant volcano of Mount St. Helens in the Cascade Range of mountains in Washington State was likely to waken from its slumbers in the near future. The Cascade Range contains the most volcanically active mountains in the USA (excluding Hawaii and Alaska), forming part of the Pacific 'Ring of Fire', a belt of active volcanoes encircling the Pacific Ocean.

carrying with it trees, sections of houses and bridges and other large pieces of debris. It was accompanied by geysers of hot gas, which smashed and burned the surrounding landscape, ripping up trees and annihilating wildlife. More than 520sq km (200sq mi) of territory was swiftly transformed into a scorched wasteland.

From the wrecked north face of the mountain, a horizontal blast of burning ash and steam shot out at up to 400km/h

In March 1980, a series of tremors at Mount St. Helens brought teams of scientific observers to study the expected eruption. Most local people were evacuated; a few diehards refused to budge, like 83-year-old Harry Truman who insisted: 'This damn mountain won't ever do me any harm…if it explodes, I'll go up with it.' Early on 18 May 1980 the mountain exploded with shattering force, leaving 62 people dead, including members of the scientific study teams – and the dogged Harry Truman, who went up with his beloved mountain as he had sworn.

DEVASTATING LANDSLIDE

The unexpected fury of the eruption was triggered in several areas at once. A moderate earthquake caused the north side of the mountain to break away, collapsing into one of the biggest landslides on record. A tide of rock debris, glacial ice, boiling water and steam came roaring down the mountainside at an estimated 250km/h (155mph), hurtled into the lake below and picked up the lake's water: all combined to form a giant mudflow,

Above: An aerial view of the spectacular eruption of Mount St. Helens volcano, May 1980.

Right: A bus partly submerged in mud from the giant landslide that was triggered by the explosive power of the volcano.
Below right: The tremendous volcanic blast felled many thousands of trees on mountains neighbouring Mount St. Helens.

(250mph), sweeping some 27km (17mi) northwards along the line of the landslide. Moments later, another blast erupted straight upwards: scientists observing the crater from a light plane narrowly escaped with their lives. The column of burning ash rose 19km (12mi) into the sky. Ash in the atmosphere darkened the skies for long distances: by mid-afternoon, visibility was down to 3m (10ft) in towns as much as 400km (250mi) distant. Ash subsequently fell all over Washington State – some 600,000 tonnes of ash descended in the area of Yakima, Washington, 145km (90mi) from the volcano – and over parts of Oregon, clogging traffic and damaging crops.

STEAMING CRATER

Before the eruption, Mount St. Helens had stood 2,950m (9,678ft) high. The blast tore 400m (1,312ft) from its height, and left a steaming crater, 3.2km (2mi) long, 1.6km (1mi) wide and 700m (2,297ft) deep. Four days after the blast President Carter visited the site of the eruption; he told reporters: 'The Moon looks like a golf course compared to what's up there.'

In 1982 the 400sq km (155sq mi) area around Mount St. Helens was designated a National Volcano Monument. It is a tourist attraction, to which vegetation and wildlife have returned. But as a US Forest Service spokesman warned: 'Nobody really knows whether it's going to start spitting thunder eggs or just go back to sleep.'

43

SLEEPING GIANTS

The vulcanologist Haroun Tazieff (1914–98), famous for his close-up films of erupting peaks, wrote: 'Those volcanoes regarded as extinct are only dead to eyes that cannot see. A thousand-year sleep is nothing to a volcano.' He warned that several great cities, including Mexico City, Seattle and Rome, were threatened by large and supposedly extinct volcanoes. Tazieff was called in by the Cameroon government in 1986, when 1,700 villagers around Lake Nyas died mysteriously after subterranean volcanic shocks. He established that the victims had been poisoned by carbon dioxide gas, liberated by the eruption and seeping from beneath the lake.

WILD WAVES: TSUNAMIS

MORE THAN 70 per cent of Earth's surface is covered by oceans, so any upheaval of the planet's crust is likely to disturb huge quantities of water, to deadly effect. The most lethal weapon the sea can hurl at landlubbers is the monster wave known as a tsunami, or seismic sea wave.

We commonly speak of giant waves as 'tidal waves', but the tsunami has nothing to do with tides. It is the sea's response to a physical jolt – an earthquake, submarine avalanche, volcanic eruption or other explosive force (including manmade nuclear blasts). In fact, it is a scaled-up version of the ripples that spread around a pond when a pebble is thrown in. Far out at sea, a tsunami may be only 30-45cm (12-18in) high, and ships far from land may barely notice it; as it nears land, however, it may build up to awesome heights: as much as 67m (220ft). In its ripple-like spreading, a tsunami may travel as far as 19,300km (12,000mi).

The deeper the water at its point of origin, the longer the wave (often several kilometres long), and it moves fastest over deeper water, achieving 185km/h (115mph) over 275m (900ft) of water, and a terrifying 1,045km/h (650mph) over a 9,150m (30,000ft) depth.

A TOWERING WALL OF WATER

As the wave approaches shallow coastal waters, it slows down and begins to build up height. When the tsunami reaches land, a towering wall of water may smash down upon coastal towns. The intensity of impact depends on the shape and structure of the coastline. Where there is deep water close to shore, or offshore coral reefs as natural breakwaters, the effect is reduced. But a shore gradually sloping upwards to shallow water enables the wave to reach catastrophic proportions. The worst scenario is a V-shaped inlet or harbour (hence the Japanese term 'tsunami', or 'harbour wave'), which funnels all the force of the tsunami into a single wave. At such places, a tsunami can deliver unimaginable destruction, killing thousands of people. Terror is increased by the fact that a tsunami rarely arrives as a single monstrous wave but as a series of waves, 15 minutes to an hour apart, which may continue their assault for hours or even days.

The sea has other terrors. Working on the surface of the water, storm winds may raise waves up to 12m (40ft) high. Variously known as surge waves, storm waves, sea surges and storm surges, these great breakers are commoner than tsunami. Most of their destructive power

is achieved by systematic pounding, but huge single waves may hit coastal installations like harbour walls with terrifying force.

MASS KILLERS

Such surge waves are mass killers: for example, at Coringa, India, in 1789, three giant, cyclone-driven surge waves drowned 20,000 persons. At Wick, Scotland, in 1872, storm waves lifted a 1,350-tonne mass of cement and iron which protected the end of a breakwater and hurled it inside the pier. A 2,600-tonne replacement block was swept away by another storm in 1877. Lighthouse records tell dramatic stories of the height which surge waves can reach – with such incidents as a 195kg (430lb) bell hurled from its position 30m (100ft) above high-water mark, or a door 60m (195ft) above sea level smashed down by a wave.

Right: Cyclone-driven waves break in fury.
Below: A sequence showing the arrival of
the Oahu tsunami at Laie Point, Hawaii,
triggered by an earthquake in Alaska in 1957.

VOYAGE OF THE 'FLYING FRIGATE'

The great earthquake which shattered Port Royal, Jamaica, in 1692, was followed by immense tsunamis crashing over the town. Some residents struggling in the water high over their housetops had a miraculous escape, when the tsunami lifted up an English frigate, the *Swan*, which was beached on its side awaiting repairs, and carried it over to them. Clutching at cables and rigging, they hauled themselves aboard, and the wave swept them on to safety over the drowned town. Sadly, the *Swan* fared less well than her unexpected passengers: the 'flying frigate' was lost at sea soon afterwards, having sailed with repairs still incomplete.

45

JAPAN'S TERRIFIC TSUNAMI

GROUND tremors go almost unnoticed in such parts of the world as Japan, where minor quakes are common. In June 1896, when crowds gathered all over the country for the annual Shinto 'Boys' Festival', people in the Sanriku district of coastal Honshu saw no reason to interrupt their celebrations for a slight tremor. No one realized that the movement came from a quake 190km (120mi) out to sea, some 9,750m (32,000ft) down in the Tuscarora Deep.

Twenty minutes after the tremor, the sea mysteriously began to ebb, receding far beyond the low-tide mark. It dragged with it boats anchored offshore, tearing them from their moorings, and left great shoals of fish stranded on mud flats. Then came the sound that alerted revellers to their danger – little more than a whisper at first, but growing to a boom as the sea rushed back in majesty. When the holidaymakers recognized their peril, a wall of water was already towering over them: a giant tsunami more than 30m (100ft) high. Then, millions of tons of water crashed down.

Racing 275km (170mi) along the coast at 80km/h (50mph), the wave forced its way nearly 160km (100mi) inland, destroying everything in its path. Entire townships were obliterated and their populations drowned. At Kamaishi, all but 143 of 4,223 buildings were swept away, along with four-fifths of the 6,500-strong population. At Hamaisi, 4,700 of the 6,500 inhabitants died. At Hongo, the only survivors were a group of old men who had skipped the festival to play a game of *Go* on a hillside above the village. A reporter sent to the disaster area travelled 48km (30mi) along a once densely-populated coast without finding any sign of life. The survivors were those

who had made it to high ground, or lived through the tsunami by clinging to pieces of floating wreckage. Crews of fishing boats far out at sea had been unaware of the deadly wave riding beneath them and returned home to an unexpected horror. To them fell the desperate task of clearing up thousands of corpses; for weeks the land was overhung with the stench of putrescence and the smoke of funeral pyres. An official survey recorded 27,122 dead and 9,247 injured, with 10,617 houses swept away.

KILLER WAVES

Japan has certainly suffered more than its fair share of tsunamis. To record only a few: in 1283 at Kamakura, more than 30,000 died by quake and tsunami; in 1703, at Awa, over 100,000 died; in 1923, Tokyo was hit by quake, fire and tsunami (see pages 24-25). Today, networks of undersea sensors are deployed to detect underwater disturbances, making an early warning system possible. For this reason, when the Sanriku district was again hit again by tsunami in 1933, many people were able to reach safety – yet 3,000 died under the 23m (75ft) killer wave. Those who live by the sea will always remain vulnerable to its anger.

WIND AND WATER

One of the worst disasters of this century was the cyclone which hit Bangladesh (East Pakistan) in November 1970. Between 300,000 and 500,000 persons died as a result of a deadly cyclone (see also pages 78-79) and the surge wave it drove before it. The inhabitants of offshore islands, many of which rise only 6m (20ft) above sea level, stood little chance before a 15m (50ft) wave – especially since cyclone warnings from an American weather satellite had been dismissed as a false alarm. When the storm hit in the middle of the night, sleeping islanders died in their beds; on one island alone, more than 20,000 perished. Next morning survivors saw the shores covered with corpses and, lacking the facilities for burial (indeed, often for their own survival), lined the beaches to push the dead back out to sea with long bamboo poles.

Below: This Japanese painting depicts wind blown waves. Earthquakes are common in Japan and are the cause of many tsunamis.

お援
七里ヶ演
風波

47

HAVOC IN CHILE...

THE SEA gods are savage – and those who live in their shadow remember this. As recently as May 1960, Mapuche Indians in central Chile responded to a killer tsunami by offering a human sacrifice, begging for 'calm in the sea and on the earth'. But the 8m (25ft), earthquake-generated wave killed 5,700 people and obliterated three fishing villages when it hit the Chilean coast.

5,000 citizens died in an earthquake followed by a tsunami that 'sank half the city beneath the waves'. The tsunami of February 1835 was witnessed by naturalist Charles Darwin, who watched from the comparative safety of his ship, *Beagle*. He wrote: 'Shortly after the shock, a great wave was seen from a distance of three or four miles [5-7km],

With their crops and fishing boats destroyed, survivors faced starvation – and an outbreak of cannibalism added to the gruesome death toll. The tsunami recoiled from the Chilean coast and raced at 835km/h (520mph) towards Japan, where it killed 150 persons. At Hilo City, Hawaii, it produced 12m (40ft) waves to smash down the sea wall, causing some $20,000,000 of damage; an efficient early warning system meant there were few lives lost.

UNDERWATER SEISMIC ACTIVITY

Many of the world's most extensive tsunami have originated off the Chilean coast, radiating nearly halfway round the world to eastern Siberia: Chile, in an area of high underwater seismic activity, has long suffered from them. The port of Valdivia was hit in December 1575, when a giant tsunami killed many and wrecked two Spanish galleons – and again in the summer of 1960. The town of Santiago was another tsunami victim in October 1562, with thousands killed.

One of Chile's most vulnerable cities, Concepción, lost thousands of citizens to tsunami in February 1570; in March 1751, both Concepción and Juan Fernandèz Island were devastated by a sequence of huge waves; in July 1757,

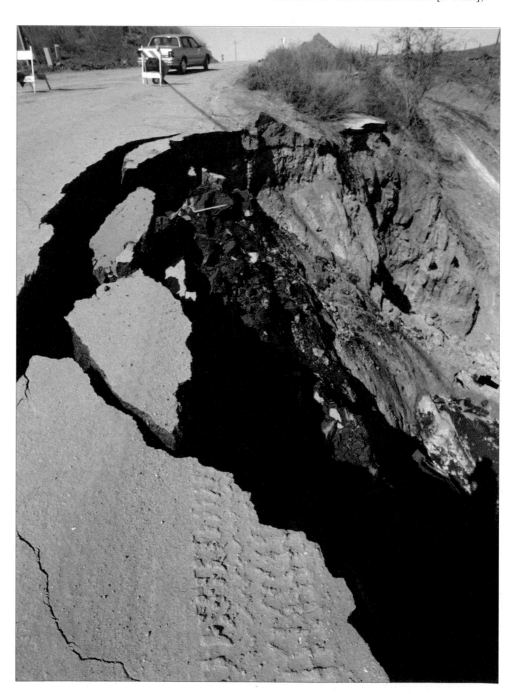

approaching in the middle of the bay with a smooth outline, but along the shore it tore up cottages and trees, as it swept onwards with irresistible force. At the head of the bay it broke into a fearful line of white breakers, which rushed up to a height of twenty-three vertical feet [7m] above the highest spring tides.' He reported that the waves travelled slowly enough for people to run to higher ground and for sailors to put to sea, hoping their boats would ride out the swell – but the tsunami claimed more than 5,000 lives.

Above: Earthquakes continue to wreak havoc on vulnerable property around the world.

... AND HELL IN HAWAII

In April 1946, an earthquake shuddered the seabed 4km (2.5mi) beneath the North Pacific, 145km (90mi) northeast of the Aleutians, triggering a mighty tsunami. A 35m (115ft), 116km/h (72mph) wave obliterated a lighthouse and its custodians on Umniak island. Then it raced south at an average of c.800km/h (500mph) and within five hours reached the Hawaiian archipelago. Many houses were smashed to matchwood – but on Oahu island, one house was carried hundreds of metres and set down in a field so gently that even the breakfast laid on the table was still in place. Worst hit was Hilo city, where 96 people drowned. Overall, the Hawaiian islands lost 159 lives and some 1,400 homes, as well as suffering some $26,000,000 damage to crops, highways and railroads, and breakwaters. The disaster inspired the creation of a Tsunami Warning System, using seismic stations and tide gauges, which proved its value in 1957, when a major tsunami claimed no lives. In 1960, however, people who ignored warnings and even went to the beach to watch the spectacle were drowned. Predictions are not infallible: in 1986, tsunami warnings drove thousands to flee to the hills to escape a wave which never arrived.

THE NETHERLANDS VERSUS THE SEA

O N THE night of 31 January 1953, storms swept the North Sea with gale-force winds of over 160km/h (100mph). Giant waves ravaged the coasts of Germany, Belgium, northern France and the Netherlands. Britain suffered some of its worst recorded gales: winds wrecked an Irish ferry with the loss of 130 lives. But it was the low-lying Netherlands that suffered worst from the storm-driven seas.

Over the centuries, the people of the Netherlands have battled using dikes and drainage to wrest thousands of square kilometres of land from the sea: today more than 60 per cent of the Dutch population lives on reclaimed land below sea level. The 1953 storm proved too much for the great stone dikes that formed the only barrier against the sea's incursion. At high tide early on the morning of 1 February, wind-driven, rain-swollen waters smashed through 100 dikes simultaneously and flooded an area of some 2,020sq km (780sq mi), leaving 133 towns and villages under water.

A HUMAN BARRICADE

At Kortgene and at Colijnsplaat, fishermen formed a human barricade against the brute force of the sea, bracing their backs for hours against the crumbling dikes to shore them up. Elsewhere, there was no escape. Thousands – many still in their nightclothes – fled for their lives to higher ground; in many cases the great waves smashed their refuge from under their feet and swept them into the flood. Others sheltered at home from the storm, unable to hear the alarm bells for the roar of the wind, and died there. In all nearly 2,000 people drowned, while many

others, marooned on rooftops and other precarious perches, died of cold before help could arrive. Rescuing 72,000 refugees soon became an international operation involving 2,000 boats and 150 planes.

A COLOSSAL FLOOD

The history of the Netherlands has been one long war between man and the North Sea. The first recorded flood occurred as long ago as 1099, caused by a combination of heavy rains, high winds and abnormally low tides: the total death toll in the lowlands and across the sea in England came to more than 100,000. Thousands more drowned in the floods of 1170, 1287 and 1228. In 1421, a colossal flood wiped out 72 villages, drowning more than 100,000, turning the

city of Dort (Dordrecht) into the island it is today. In the 16th century, the country suffered three more disastrous floods – and one useful one: in 1574, floodwaters burst the dikes and engulfed the Spanish forces besieging the city of Leiden (Leyden), drowning 20,000 Spanish soldiers and literally sweeping the Spanish out of Holland. But in 1646 (110,000 drowned) and 1916 (at least 10,000 dead), it was the Dutch who suffered again.

Each time, the Dutch responded by rebuilding the dikes more strongly – and always, ultimately, in vain. The catastrophic floods of 1953 forced them to take decisive action to guard the exposed coastline more securely. In 1958, engineers began work on the ambitious Delta Project, sealing off most of the delta's large inlets with barrier dams at a cost of some $5 billion. It was completed in 1985: 30km (18.5mi) of dams now guard the coast, complemented by a 9km (5.6mi) storm-surge barrier of 62 massive, movable steel gates hanging from huge concrete pillars, which can be closed when a flood threatens.

Right: Britain also battles against high tides and storms in the North Sea. This picture shows floods in Norfolk in 1912.

THE DIKES HELD

In February 1995, the threat of flood came not from the sea but from the swollen Rhine and Meuse rivers, flowing from Germany and France into the east Netherlands. Amid fears that river dikes would not withstand the huge pressure of floodwaters, more than 250,000 people were evacuated from the area. This time, the dikes held and the evacuees were able to return home, while the government made hasty plans to speed up a river dike reinforcement programme.

CHINA'S SORROW

THE RICH plains beside a river provide fertile land where farmers prosper – but there is a price to be paid. From time to time, the river is likely to overflow its banks, taking back its bounty and, often, charging interest in terms of human lives. They call the Huanghe (Hwang Ho; Yellow River) 'China's Sorrow'. Its fertile plains provide vital farmland, but its mighty waters, held back only by thousands of 'homemade' dikes, have burst their banks more than 1,500 times to wreak havoc, leaving millions dead and millions more homeless and starving.

The problem is that the Huanghe is probably the world's muddiest river. On its c.4,180km (2,600mi) meandering course from Tibet to the Yellow Sea, it picks up the yellow silt which gives it its name at a rate of around 1.6 billion tonnes a year. Winding across China's plains, it dumps much of its load along its own bed. Thus, instead of cutting a deeper channel over the centuries, as many rivers do, it builds up its bed until it overflows its banks. Since early times, the Chinese have fought back with barricades, building a series of huge ramparts set as much as 13km (8mi) back from each bank. By the 19th century, constant reinforcement of these dikes with mud and plant material had raised them in places to a height of c.9m (30ft), on a base perhaps 30m (100ft) wide; thus, the river itself often flowed high above the farms and villages below.

THE GREATEST FLOOD IN HISTORY

By September 1887, the massive but brittle dikes represented a disaster waiting to happen; then heavy rains started them crumbling. As the embankments collapsed, they unleashed the greatest flood in recorded history. The Huanghe rampaged across the plains, sweeping away at least 1,500 communities, drowning farmland under a vast lake. 'The worst flood since Noah' may have killed as many as 2,500,000 people, leaving millions more facing a two-year famine on the devastated plain.

52

Above: This picture shows a gap in the Great Wall of China at Shan-Hai-Kwan which was caused by the severe annual floods.

Grimly, an army of workers rebuilt the dikes; but they could contain the Huanghe only temporarily. In the 1930s the river broke through again, drowning 88,000sq km (34,000sq mi) of land, killing tens of thousands and leaving some 80,000,000 homeless. In 1938, the Chinese Nationalist army deliberately destroyed dikes to halt the invading Japanese, causing widespread flooding throughout North China in which 500,000 Chinese died and millions more once again faced starvation.

Another great Chinese river, the 5,470km (3,400mi)-long Changjiang (Yangtze), is also prone to catastrophic flooding. When it broke its banks in 1911, it drowned 100,000 people, and condemned an equal number to death by starvation as a direct result of the destruction caused. Flooding in 1931 caused the death of 140,000; a further 57,000 lives were lost in 1949. In August 1950, both the Changjiang and the 2,655km (1,650mi)-long Xihe (Hwai; West River) overflowed their banks, drowning some 20,200sq km (7,800sq mi) of farmland for months. Chinese official figures of 489 drowned may be a gross underestimate; 10,000,000 folk were driven from their homes and more than 890,000 dwellings were totally destroyed. The Changjiang and Xihe overflowed again in 1954, claiming 40,000 lives and leaving a million homeless.

EXTENSIVE FLOODING

In 1981, the Changjiang's flooding was exacerbated in Sichuan province because for three decades land on the river's upper reaches had been systematically deforested to create more arable land. Without trees to act as a natural control on the flow of summer rainfall into the river's tributaries, the streams swelled mightily, sweeping tons of topsoil as well as water to the Changjiang. The great river was already high when early July brought three days of heavy rain – the last straw for its embankments. Raging floods smashed buildings, roads and bridges. A massive tide slammed down the Changjiang gorges to strike the Gezhou Dam with a 5.5m (18ft) wave. The dam held, but the water 'rebounded' to cause more floods. The bare hands of 200,000 workers, frantically shoring up dikes, saved millions of lives, but nonetheless 1,300 people were dead or missing, 28,000 injured, and 1,500,000 homeless.

FATHER OF WATERS

THE GREAT rivers of the USA have produced their share of catastrophic floods; but one of the most notorious American floods originated in a less well-known waterway, the Conemaugh River. In May 1889, an ill-maintained dam at South Fork Reservoir, Pennsylvania gave way, unleashing some 20.5 billion litres (4.5 billion gallons) of water on to Johnstown, 19km (12mi) away.

The flood wiped out five smaller towns en route; estimates of the number of dead range from 2,500 to as high as 8,000. The tragedy aroused great bitterness against the 'millionaires' club' which enjoyed fishing rights on the reservoir but had failed to maintain the dam: one survivor who attacked them in verse wrote, 'All the horrors that hell could wish/Such was the price that was paid – for fish.'

But the real queen of floods is the Mississippi River, which Native Americans called the 'Father of Waters'. To European settlers its flood cycles were just another natural obstacle to be overcome, and in the 18th century they began trying to control its lower reaches with a patchwork of levees (embankments) to protect their fields. The river repeatedly broke through the levees to flood the land; and the levees were rebuilt, higher and stronger. Mississippi River Control engineers never seemed to realize that the better they built their barriers, the stronger the water pressure that built up against them. Between 1858 and 1922, the river beat them 11 times.

April 1874 saw one of the great river's worst overspills, flooding tens of thousands of hectares in the Mississippi Valley and drowning some 300 people. In 1912 the river overflowed levees everywhere, turning large tracts of Mississippi, Kentucky and Illinois into inland lakes, drowning 250 and leaving 30,000 homeless. But the engineers continued to put their trust in the levee system, which grew to form a 1,610km (1,000mi) wall of earth on both sides of the river from Cairo, Illinois, to the Gulf of Mexico.

WAVES BROKE THROUGH

Autumn 1926 brought heavy rainfalls to the Mississippi basin, persisting through winter into spring. The river rose ominously; but early in April 1927 engineers were still claiming that 'We are in a position to hold all the water in sight.' They were not. On 21 April, the levee gave way at Mound Landing, Mississippi, and the river romped over some 8,100sq km (3,120sq mi) of the state. Witnesses described waves breaking through in a 'tan-coloured wall seven feet [2.1m] high', with a roaring sound many likened to a tornado. Soon the floodwaters had breached their retaining walls in more than 100 places to form a vast inland sea. By May more than 64,770sq km (25,000sq mi) of land was underwater, including half Arkansas and much of Mississippi and Louisiana. The *New York Times* reported that '...the state of Arkansas is no longer visible'. Some 300 people drowned, along with 162,000 head of livestock and 1,000,000 chickens. More than 750,000 were left homeless and property damages were reckoned at $285 million. In mid-May New Orleans was in serious danger, and was saved only when engineers diverted

the floodwaters by blowing up a nearby levee, draining the waters towards the Gulf. The floods did not ebb until July.

FLOOD PREVENTION

In 1928, a $325 million programme began to reinforce the dike system with reservoirs, dams and spillways to prevent such another disaster. But as Mark Twain had remarked: 'One who knows the Mississippi will promptly aver…that ten thousand River Commissions, with the mines of the world at their back, cannot tame that lawless stream.' Subsequent floods have been less catastrophic, but they continue. The floods of 1993 were estimated to have caused $10 billion worth of damage.

All pictures: Floods are often unexpected and cause catastrophic damage.

HOUR OF HORROR

In June 1903, a sudden violent cloudburst over the foothills of Oregon's Blue Mountains converted the quiet Willow Creek into a raging torrent, sending a 7.6m (25ft) wall of water cascading onto the town of Heppner. In the course of a single hour, the flash flood destroyed one-third of Heppner's buildings and drowned 325 people.

FLORENCE BENEATH THE WATERS

THE ITALIAN city of Florence is a treasure-house of the art of the European Renaissance, famed for its architecture, museums, galleries and libraries. In 1966 the world learned how vulnerable a treasure-house can be in the face of natural forces. Florence stands on the Arno River, which has had a history of flooding since the 12th century. In fact, by 1545 the river's threat was obvious enough to set Leonardo da Vinci to work on plans to control it by a series of dams, locks and lakes.

Da Vinci's scheme was never put into effect, and matters were made worse by woodcutters clearing trees that would have helped to retain water in the soil – a practice which has continued throughout Italy until today, when most of the country's hills are deforested. The Arno continued to assail Florence with major floods almost every century.

November 1966 brought torrential rains which swelled the rivers of northern Italy to danger point. In only two days, 48cm (19in) of rain was recorded – more than the area would normally expect in four months. The Arno rose up in raging spate, overspilling its banks to inundate 750 villages as well as the cities of Venice, Pisa and Florence. Human error componded the effect: the custodians of the Arno's hydroelectric dams above Florence opened their floodgates too late and unleashed a towering wall of water.

THE BRIDGE WAS SUBMERGED

While the citizens of Florence slept, the waters rushed into their city, raising the level of the river by 5.5m (18ft) in just two hours, until it thundered only 1m (3ft) below the famous Ponte Vecchio bridge. Nightwatchmen first raised the alarm, summoning shopkeepers to the bridge to rescue their wares from the shops that are built on the bridge itself. Soon the bridge was submerged, and appeared likely to share the fate of the original Ponte Vecchio, destroyed by the disastrous flood of 1333. At daybreak, Florentines rose to find water surging outside their doors – and still rising. Soon the city was cut off from the rest of the world, its bridges, roads and railways blocked or washed away, its power and telephone lines down. Still the waters rose, drowning Florence in a thick, dark lake befouled by the ruptured sewage system. In some parts of the city the water reached the ceilings of upstairs rooms, eventually surpassing all former flood records by more than 60cm (2ft). Florentines fled to upper floors and scrambled onto rooftops; more than 100,000 persons were trapped in their homes for days – and 149 were drowned. When the river withdrew, half a million tonnes of mud, oil, silt and sewage covered the city. A massive rescue operation was launched by ten European countries to help the stranded, homeless and starving.

ART TREASURES DESTROYED

While refugees fled for their lives, the river wreaked havoc on the world's greatest collection of Renaissance art. At the Biblioteca Nazionale Centrale, one million books and manuscripts were destroyed. Inside the Church of Santa Croce, a 6m (20ft) tide drowned the

tombs of Michelangelo, Galileo, Rossini and Macchiavelli. Frescoes were destroyed, paintings marred by filthy water, and buildings damaged. Rescue parties of students – nicknamed 'Blue Angels' from their blue jeans – formed human chains to pass water-logged books from the flooded basement of the Biblioteca to upper floors, to be sent to tobacco-drying kilns in central Italy. Scholars and restoration experts from all over the world came to aid in the rescue work, but much was ruined beyond repair.

SHOCKING ART

Italy and the world suffered the loss of more irreplaceable art treasures on 26 September 1997, when two earth tremors shook the region of Umbria. Among the buildings brought down was the Upper Church of the 700-year-old Basilica of St. Francis, at Assisi. Two Franciscan friars and two surveyors died when the building collapsed, and large areas of magnificent fresco cycles attributed to Giovanni Cimabué (c.1240–1302) and his pupil Giotto (c.1266–1337), the founding fathers of Western European art, were reduced to rubble and dust.

Below: Severe flooding of the River Arno threatens Florence during the winter of 1864.

57

LIGHTNING: WRATH OF THE GODS

A SEARING FLASH that lights up the sky, followed by an earth-shaking roar: it is hardly surprising that in ancient times and among primitive peoples humans often regarded lightning as a sign of the wrath of their god or gods. The Ancient Greeks considered lightning and its subsequent 'thunderbolt' as the weapons of Zeus, the father god, and regarded any site struck by lightning as sacred. The Persian ruler Xerxes noted that 'his [God's] missiles always smite the largest buildings and trees…for God loves to truncate all things that rise too high.'

The lightning flash we see is the 'return stroke', which rises from the ground along the track of the first 'leader', at a speed of up to 140,000km/sec (87,000mi/sec). The flash may vary in length from less than 90m (300ft) to as much as 32km (20mi). The average flash endures for only 0.25 seconds, but a persistent image on the retina of the eye makes it appear longer-lasting to human viewers. Superheating, leading to rapid expansion and contraction of air in the lightning's path, causes the thunderclap.

Some North American Indian tribes revered the 'Thunderbird', believing that the lightning flashed from his eyes. We must conclude that the deity (or deities) are in a permanent rage, since it is estimated that every second some 600 lightning bolts strike the Earth, which experiences an average of 45,000 thunderstorms per day.

STATIC ELECTRICITY

The lowering cumulonimbus clouds associated with thunderstorms are the major producers of lightning. Static electricity is generated in them, perhaps by the collision of water particles in accelerated air currents: meteorologists disagree on the exact cause. Discharge takes place in the form of lightning. Its most spectacular, and most common, form is called forked or streak lightning. A cloud-to-ground flash begins with a negatively-charged zigzag 'leader' stroke blasting from the cloud base, which may travel at about 1,600km/sec (1,000mi/sec); when it comes within about 100m (330ft) of the ground, a positively-charged 'leader' leaps from the ground to meet it.

Above: 'And there came down fire from heaven…' A thunderbolt from God. (II Kings 1: 10).

58

PERIL ON THE SEA

One of the most dangerous places to be during a thunderstorm is on water in a wooden boat. The first wooden ship fitted with a 'lightning rod' was the explorer Captain James Cook's *Endeavour* in 1768–71. Cook reported that it saved the ship from destruction on at least one occasion – but lightning remained a major cause of loss (more than 35 British ships were destroyed by lightning in the period 1810–15) until 1846, when the British Navy adopted the practice of running copper strips the length of the masts and connecting them to copper plates on the hull and keel to act as lightning conductors.

Right: The spectacular power of lightning.

Since the electrical potential of the 'gap' where the negative and positive charges strive to form a conducting path has been estimated at up to 100 million volts, it is not surprising that non- or poorly-conductive matter, like wood, suffers worst from lightning strikes. Considering the frequency of strikes, humans get off relatively lightly: exact statistics are scarce, but it is estimated that in the USA about 150 persons are killed annually by lightning, and several hundred injured. More serious is its fire-rising potential (see also pages 86-87): some 10,000 forest fires every year are caused by lightning in the USA alone. It is, of course, a myth that 'lightning never strikes twice in the same place': the tower of New York's Empire State Building averages 23 strikes a year; one individual in the USA is reliably recorded to have been struck by lightning seven times – suffering only minor burns.

PROS AND CONS OF CONDUCTORS

Metal rods called lightning conductors provide a low-resistance path for the lightning's discharge of energy, thus protecting any structure of which they form the highest point. The American polymath Benjamin Franklin (1706–90) erected the first lightning conductor, his own invention, on his house in Philadelphia in 1752. Use of the device spread quickly – but not without opposition. The Reverend Doctor Price of Boston denounced lightning conductors as a defiance of the wrath of God, and blamed them for the earthquakes that shook Massachusetts in 1755. The French priest and physicist Jean Nollet (1700–70) claimed that conductors would draw down lightning to destroy the buildings they were intended to protect.

DEATH IN A FLASH

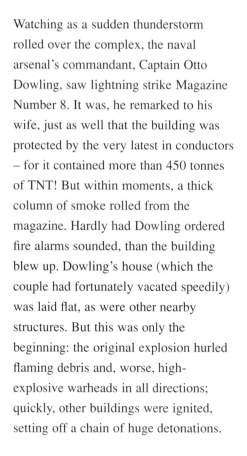

THE GREATEST detonation of explosives in the history of the USA – and, until the atomic destruction of Japanese cities in 1945, perhaps the greatest in the history of the world – ripped apart a rural area of upstate New Jersey on a sunny Saturday afternoon in July 1926. Near the town of Dover, a region of rolling hills and tranquil lakes was also the site for the US Navy's Lake Denmark Naval Ammunition Depot and the Army's Picatinny Arsenal; in all, some 30 buildings in which lay about one-third of the nation's stock of munitions.

personnel and civilians in nearby residential areas, were injured. Of the arsenal's 180 buildings, only 16 were left standing: all structures within 850m (2,800ft) of the original explosion were vaporized; buildings up to 7,000m (4.3mi) away suffered severe structural damage. The successive blasts were heard and felt up to 80km (50mi) away.

Many aircraft and airships – particularly in the earlier days of aviation, when non-conductive wood and fabric were major structural components

Watching as a sudden thunderstorm rolled over the complex, the naval arsenal's commandant, Captain Otto Dowling, saw lightning strike Magazine Number 8. It was, he remarked to his wife, just as well that the building was protected by the very latest in conductors – for it contained more than 450 tonnes of TNT! But within moments, a thick column of smoke rolled from the magazine. Hardly had Dowling ordered fire alarms sounded, than the building blew up. Dowling's house (which the couple had fortunately vacated speedily) was laid flat, as were other nearby structures. But this was only the beginning: the original explosion hurled flaming debris and, worse, high-explosive warheads in all directions; quickly, other buildings were ignited, setting off a chain of huge detonations.

30 PEOPLE KILLED

Only the fact that, on a Saturday afternoon, just a skeleton staff was on duty prevented great loss of life: the total death toll was only 30 persons, although several hundred, including service

Left and above: It is estimated that every second some 600 lightning bolts strike the Earth. Forked lightning is the most common form.

61

– have been destroyed as a result of thunderstorms, but their destruction has more often been due to air turbulence or loss of visibility than to lightning strikes. A modern exception was Pan American Airlines' Clipper Flight 214, as it flew in a holding pattern near Philadelphia, Pennsylvania, during a thunderstorm on the evening of 8 December 1963.

A PLUNGING FIREBALL

Eyewitnesses on the ground and in a nearby National Airlines plane clearly saw the Being 707 swiftly transformed into a plunging fireball after a lightning strike on its port wing. All 81 persons aboard were killed. Since metal aircraft are highly conductive, the usual result of a lightning strike is no more than a hole

the size of a five-penny piece burnt in the metal skin. In the case of Clipper 214, however, it was found that the lightning had ignited the explosive blend of fuel and air in a reserve wing tank.

LIFE-GIVING STROKES

Lightning is not a totally destructive force. Its discharge releases nitrogen in the atmosphere, and this is carried down by raindrops to enrich Earth's soil. According to some scientists, in the earliest days of Earth lightning may have helped to create living matter by triggering the formation of complex chemical compounds from basic elements.

QUICK ON THE TRIGGER

Although metal aircraft are unlikely to be destroyed by lightning, their high conductivity makes them likely to be stuck because of 'trigger effect'. This occurs when a highly conductive object occupies the gap between the lightning's positive and negative strokes (as was the case with the ill-fated Clipper 214). The trigger effect resulted in damage (fortunately very minor) to the Saturn launch vehicle of the *Apollo 12* space mission: as it climbed from Cape Canaveral on 14 November 1969, the 110m (360ft) rocket was struck by lightning at 1,800m (6,000ft) and 3,900m (13,000ft).

LOST SUMMERS AND 'HARD RAINS'

IN THE freak summer of 1992, the state of Colorado, USA, experienced several days of freezing temperatures in June, with snow storms severe enough to close three mountain highways. Paris was brought to a halt by torrential rainstorms. In May, Hong Kong suffered one of the heaviest downpours on record: 110mm (4.3in) of rain in one hour turned streets into rivers and killed five people.

Scientists attributed much of the unseasonable weather to the effects of the eruption of Mount Pinatubo in the Philippines on 13 June 1991 (one of the largest volcanic explosions of the 20th century). This hurled some 20,000,000 tonnes of gas and ash into the stratosphere, to form a global haze resulting in lowered temperatures worldwide.

The hazards of 1992, however, pale into insignificance beside those of 'the summer that never was'. This fell in the year 1816, towards the end of the 'Little Ice Age' of c.1400–1850, during which the mean temperature was some 2-4°C (4-7°F) lower than today. Although people in 1816 did not know it, much of their suffering was, like the freak weather of 1992, probably caused by debris thrown up by volcanic eruptions: Mount Soufrière in the West Indies in 1812; Mount Mayon, Philippines, in 1814; and Mount Tambora, Java, in April 1815. The last-named eruption killed around 10,000

All pictures: Freak storms of snow and hail have occurred throughout history.

persons immediately and caused a famine that claimed some 80,000 further victims.

ABNORMALLY COLD WEATHER

During the spring and summer of 1816, abnormally cold weather – still the coldest summer ever recorded in places as widely separated as Connecticut, USA, and Geneva, Switzerland – with snow, killing frosts and heavy rain, combined to blight crops all over Europe

and in northeast America, where snowdrifts up to 50cm (20in) deep were reported in Vermont in June. Food prices rocketed, and France, England (where protesters paraded under banners reading 'Bread or Blood') and Scotland saw savage riots, during which food stores were looted. Ireland experienced its worst famine until that of 1845 (see pages 88-89), followed by a typhus epidemic that had claimed an estimated 50,000 victims by 1818. Worst affected was Switzerland, hub of the European grain trade, where a year-long famine claimed many lives. Coming as it did immediately after the destructive Napoleonic Wars, the lost harvest of 1816 led directly to the great European economic depression of 1818–19.

Although never a killer on the scale described above, hail – precipitation in the form of ice particles – has also claimed victims. Happily, no one was struck by the largest hailstone in American records, a 766g (1.7lb) monster that fell in Coffeyville, Kansas, on 3 September 1970, but although hailstones are generally below 1cm (0.4in) in diameter, a storm may be deadly. The Indian subcontinent has undergone the worst reliably recorded hailstorms: one in 1853 killed 84 people and 3,000 cattle; 250 persons were killed by hail on 30 April 1888; and on 14 April 1986, hailstones up to 13cm (5in) in diameter and weighing more than 500g (1.1lb) battered to death 92 people in the Gopalganji district of Bangladesh. Even when hailstorms, which may cover limited areas to a depth of more than 30cm (12in), claim no human victims, they often severely damage crops.

63

WAR ON THE ICE

In the later 1980s – early 1990s, Indian and Pakistani troops waged an undeclared war in one of the most inhospitable regions of Earth, the glaciers of the Karakoram mountains in northern Kashmir. Although no official figures have been released, it is known that several hundred men died in the conflict and thousands were wounded. What has been admitted was that although soldiers on both sides were given at least six weeks training in winter survival, temperatures often falling to below -25°C (-43°F), blinding, week-long blizzards, and avalanches were responsible for 80 per cent of all casualties.

THE GREAT STORMS OF BRITAIN

ALTHOUGH IT is said to be the nation's main topic of conversation, Britain's weather is generally less than sensational; at least, when compared to conditions in other countries, as described elsewhere in these pages. Sometimes, however, the weather really gives the British people something to talk about.

Tongues certainly must have wagged in London after the great gale (possibly a tornado) of 23 October 1091, which destroyed the stone-and-timber church of St Mary le Bow (later the site of the true Cockney's 'Bow Bells') and some 600 dwellings. A church was again the major target of heavenly wrath in October 1638, when a lightning strike on the church at Widecombe-in-the-Moor,

Below: The Great Storm on 16 October 1987 devastated many ancient British woodlands.

Devon, was followed by 'a fireball' and a great wind that battered worshippers against the church's stone walls, killing 50 and injuring 12.

'Horror and confusion seized upon all,' recorded Daniel Defoe. 'No pen can describe it, no tongue can express it.' Nevertheless, he went on to give a dramatic account of the Great Storm of 1703 – a hurricane that began on the night of 26 November and raged for about five days. As well as destroying or badly damaging some 5,000 dwellings in

BRITISH 'TWISTERS'

'Twisters' are popularly identified with the USA – but the country with the highest frequency of reported tornadoes per square kilometre is Britain. On 21 November 1981, central England experienced 105 tornadoes within a few hours, a European record. However, most of Britain's tornadoes are so mild that they go unnoticed. The Selsey, Sussex, tornado of 8 January 1998, although sensationalized by the press, was officially classified as 'weak' – at T3 (93-114mph) on the Tornado Intensity Scale. Fewer than 0.01 per cent of tornadoes worldwide reach T10 (270-299mph) force.

64

southern England, it killed an estimated 8,000 persons – mostly sailors in coastal waters, where the first Eddystone Lighthouse was toppled – and injured many more. A notable casualty was the Bishop of Wells, killed in bed with his wife when their chimney stack was blown down on them.

AN ECOLOGICAL DISASTER

A major casualty of Britain's second Great Storm – on 16 October 1987 – was the credibility of the London Weather Centre, whose television 'weather man' had scoffed at the idea that severe winds were rising. A Force 11 gale proceeded to cause some £200,000,000-worth (at 1998 values) of damage to property, killing 18 persons and injuring many. It was an ecological disaster: as well as the tens of thousands of mature trees destroyed – among them six of the great and ancient oak trees that gave the Kentish town of

Sevenoaks its name – the famous arboretum at Kew Gardens, London, sustained damage that it was (at first; recovery proved swifter than expected) estimated would take 200 years to repair.

Even more severe, although – perhaps because it was correctly forecast by the experts – less well-remembered, was the 'Burns Day' (25 January) storm of 1990, which affected most of the United

Above: Trees were toppled and buildings suffered structural damage during the storm. 18 people died as gale-force winds struck.

Kingdom. Some 50 people died, including some in small craft sunk in coastal waters, millions more trees fell, and the total cost of repairing damage to property was estimated at £4,000,000 (1998 values).

CORNWALL FEARS THE SUN'S ECLIPSE

Cornwall's local authorities are anticipating a 'natural disaster' of an unusual kind on 11 August 1999. On that day, the first total eclipse of the Sun visible from the British mainland since June 1927 (an event not occurring again until September 2090) will be seen from an area lying between Plymouth and Land's End. Some 500,000 people are expected to travel to Cornwall to view the phenomenon – joining 500,000 conventional holidaymakers already there. Record traffic jams, mountains of rubbish, lack of accommodation, ecological damage, medical emergencies caused by over-enthusiastic viewers who incur eye damage, and even hooliganism if rain or cloud spoil the spectacle, are predicted to put a massive strain on Cornwall's services.

LONDON'S PARTICULAR MENACE

L ONDON'S FIRST attempt to limit air pollution dates back to a royal proclamation of 1306, imposing 'great fines and ransoms' on craftsmen whose workshops emitted noxious fumes. In 1661 the diarist John Evelyn denounced 'impure and thick mist…horrid Smoake…which fouls our Clothes, and corrupts the Waters…[causing] catarrhs, coughs, and consumptions [to] rage more in this one City than in the whole Earth.' He was describing London's fog, then largely caused by the soot from thousands of soft-coal fires.

By the 19th century, as industrialization increased, fog was perhaps the city's major characteristic; nationwide, the capital was known as 'the Big Smoke'. Described as 'a London particular', fog plays a leading part in Charles Dickens's *Bleak House* (1852), while Sir Arthur Conan Doyle often sent out Sherlock Holmes to hunt down malefactors in dense 'pea-soupers'. In fact, London's fogs killed far more citizens, largely through the aggravation of respiratory ailments, than all Dickens's and Conan Doyle's villains.

In November 1879–March 1880, near-impenetrable fog cloaked London for four months with hardly a break. In 1887, leading scientists urged a ban on coal fires, advocating that all cooking and heating should be by gas (a Public Health Act in 1875 had limited smoke emission from industrial sources). By 1905, when emissions from motor vehicles were adding a further ingredient to the deadly atmospheric cocktail, one Dr. Des Vouex coined the word 'smog' (smoke and fog) to describe the poisonous cloud that forms over urban areas, especially in times of high humidity and little wind. In the period around World War II, further smoke abatement legislation, and the increasing availability of smokeless fuels, promised significantly to curb air pollution.

THE YEAR OF THE 'GREAT STINK'

Perhaps the only good word ever said for fog was in autumn 1858, during 'the Great Stink of London'. A combination of very hot, dry, windless weather, added to the discharge of raw sewage into the Thames, wrapped the city in a smell so bad that there was discussion of moving Parliament and the Law Courts to Oxford for the duration. One Dr. Alfred Carpenter, addressing the Royal Society of Arts, claimed that London's fog was the only thing that reduced the smell, by trapping it at water-level so that it could not circulate. In fact, it was at last cured by large quantities of slaked lime – and some timely rainstorms.

KILLER SMOGS

Yet in December 1952 London experienced the worst of all its killer smogs. A warm air mass from the Atlantic stalled above the city; cooler, moist air trapped below it produced the heat inversion ideal for smog formation. Choking, yellowish fog, carrying particles of soot and sulphur dioxide, thickened by chemical and petrol fumes, blanketed London for the better part of a

66

week. With visibility often less than 1m (3ft), transport was thrown into chaos, air flights were cancelled and dozens died in road accidents; fog penetrated cinemas and theatres, stopping the shows. Far more serious was the effect on those with respiratory weaknesses, especially elderly people. Some 4,000 persons died (almost literally choking to death) while the fog persisted; the deaths of 8,000 more are ascribed to its lingering effect.

The immediate result was the Clean Air Act of 1956, imposing smokeless zones in urban areas. Coal fires would cause no more killer smogs – but the legislation had to be updated after December 1962, when heat inversion led to a smog polluted with sulphur dioxide from industrial processes causing the deaths of 136 elderly Londoners in four days and hospitalizing more than 1,000 persons.

Below: In the 19th century, fogs and smogs were common in London. Coal fires and increased industrialization were responsible for the poor quality of the capital's air, and many people, particularly those with respiratory weaknesses, died as a result.

SMOG YESTERDAY; SMOG TODAY

The USA's first smoke abatement legislation was enacted by the Chicago city council in 1881. In spite of this pioneering act, Chicago remains one of America's nine most polluted cities: the others, according to recent statistics, are Baltimore, Hartford, Houston, Los Angeles, Milwaukee, New York, Philadelphia and San Diego. Los Angeles (challenged by Athens and Tokyo) has the unenviable reputation of the smog capital of the world. The major culprit today is 'petrochemical smog', caused by chemical reaction between vehicle emissions and sunlight, which irritates sensitive membranes in the human body, notably those of the eyes, nose and throat, as well as blighting vegetation.

AMERICA'S 'WHITE HURRICANES'

IN 1958, the US Weather Bureau defined a blizzard as a storm characterized by heavy snow, gales of 56km/h (35mph) or more, and visibility below 0.4km (0.25mi); these conditions enduring for at least three hours. Although Americans in 1888 did not judge by these criteria, they were in no doubt about the killer wind that chilled them in March of that year: it has entered American folklore as the 'Great White Hurricane', or simply 'the Blizzard of '88'.

The cataclysm was triggered by the collision of two mighty weather fronts – a mass of Arctic air driven by 130km/h (80mph) gales from northwest Canada; a warm, wet front moving up from the Gulf of Mexico – in the Atlantic off Delaware. The cold mass prevailed, and by the afternoon of 11 March 1888 howling gales were playing havoc with shipping in Chesapeake Bay and driving great snowclouds inland over the northeastern states. By the evening, the blizzard reached New York City, which it was to lash for nearly three days.

With winds gusting up to 145km/h (90mph) and snow falling 'as if people were pouring buckets of flour from the rooftops', the metropolis, and an area around it of some 160km (100mi) radius, was brought to a standstill. Horse-drawn streetcars were blown from their tracks; zero visibility on the elevated railway led to collisions and then suspension of services, stranding some 15,000 passengers in unheated carriages. Some workers who attempted to struggle to their jobs paid for their loyalty with their lives: their frozen corpses were later dug out of 6m (20ft)-deep snowdrifts. In all, more than 400 persons died in the blizzard (some 200 in New York City alone), and about 200 ships and small craft were wrecked.

Below: An ice-covered boat awaits the thaw.

A MASSIVE SNOWSTORM

The 53.1cm (20.9in) snowfall in 30 hours, recorded in New York in the 1888 blizzard, was not eclipsed until 1947. Then, on 26 December, a massive snowstorm briefly paralyzed New York by depositing 65.5cm (25.8in) of snow within seven hours. The icy gales of 1888 were lacking; even so, 55 persons died, some in fires caused by power lines downed by weight of snow. In February 1958, blizzards hit all across the eastern states: in the worst, on 15-16 February, more than 500 people died over an area extending from Maine to Virginia. The entire eastern USA was again affected by the 'storm of the century', the 'snow-a-cane', the 'storm with the heart of a blizzard and the soul of a hurricane', on 12-14 March 1993. Twelve states declared a state of emergency; all air and surface traffic, from Boston, Massachusetts, to Atlanta, Georgia, was at a standstill; 53.3cm (21in) of snow fell in Birmingham, Alabama; around 130 persons died, and damage was estimated at $1.2 billion.

Right and below: Snow blizzards cause havoc.

THE DEADLY ICE-STORM

An ice-storm is a prolonged period of freezing rain ('glaze'). This is formed when a warm air mass passes over a stagnant body of cold air in the lower atmosphere; rain from the warm mass does not freeze in the cold air because of its surface tension, but when it strikes a solid object, disrupting its surface tension, it freezes immediately. One of the worst ice-storms on record struck Canada and the northeastern USA in January 1998. More than 3,000,000 Canadians were left without heating when power lines were brought down by the weight of accumulated ice; and some 20 deaths were attributed to temperatures as low as -31°C (-13°F). Livestock froze where they stood-and the future of Canada's maple syrup industry was threatened by the loss of an estimated 20,000,000 trees, part of a damages bill reckoned at around $2 billion.

COLD FEET IN ALASKA

The world's record low-temperature reading is generally accepted to be -89.2°C (-128.6°F), recorded in Antarctica in 1983. Although temperatures in Alaska in February 1989, during the state's worst cold wave on reliable record, did not fall quite so low, the aptly named town of Coldfoot, 80km (50mi) inside the Arctic Circle, claimed an (unconfirmed) record North American low of -99°C (-82°F).

BIG WINDS: BIG TROUBLE

HURRICANE, typhoon, cyclone, tornado: these are words that call up images of frightening power, uncontrollable violence unleashed. No wonder that they have all been used as names or nicknames for military aircraft, like the immortal Hawker Hurricane of World War II, powerful sports cars, boxers, even 'miracle detergents'!

Hurricanes and typhoons are, in fact, both manifestations of the storm known as a cyclone, which is formed when very high winds circle around an area of low atmospheric pressure. The circular movement is anticlockwise north of the Equator; clockwise south of the Equator. Middle latitude cyclones, lesser in force, may form over land or water; tropical cyclones form over the warm waters of the equatorial zones. A cyclone centring on an area of unusually low pressure may reach the pitch of severity where it is named a hurricane (in the Atlantic Ocean or Caribbean), a typhoon (in the Pacific Ocean), a tropical cyclone (in the Indian Ocean), or a baguio (in the Philippines). One of these storms, characterized by winds of up to 480km/h (300mph), savage rainstorms and huge, wind-driven waves, may extend over a radius of as much as 800km (500mi). At its centre lies an area of calm averaging about 24km (15km) in diameter: in this 'eye of the cyclone' the winds are still and the sky clear.

THREAT TO SHIPPING

The greatest threat of cyclones, hurricanes and typhoons is to shipping and coastal regions; inland areas suffer

NAMING THE WINDS

The word 'hurricane' is said to stem from Huracan, the storm god of the indigenous Caribbean Indians. 'Typhoon' may come either from *da feng*, Mandarin Chinese for 'great wind', or from Typhon, an earth-giant of Classical legend. In Australia, hurricanes are sometimes called by their Aboriginal name: 'willy-willy'.

Left and above: The dangers of tornadoes.

HURRICANE STRENGTH AND SPEED

The strength of hurricanes is rated from Category 1 (winds of at least 120km/h/75mph, or Force 12 on the Beaufort Scale) to Category 5 (winds rising above 250km/h/155mph). Their rate of travel varies from 8km/h (5mph) to 80km/h (50mph); thus, a hurricane may take as long as 12-18 hours to clear a single coastal area.

70

more from tornadoes. A tornado, or 'twister', is formed when updrafts of warm air, typically formed in a thundercloud, are affected by winds veering at different speeds and levels. These cause the air to rotate, as the stronger high-level winds remove air faster than it is supplied by lesser winds at low level. The result is a column formed by strong winds rotating in a upward spiral, with a lighter descending wind at the centre. When the column's base touches the ground, it generates suction that can rip up trees, tear off roofs, and haul heavy objects skywards. Similar conditions over water may create a waterspout.

Below: Hurricanes, typhoons, tornadoes, cyclones – they all mean one thing; trouble.

NO 'HURRICANE SADDAM HUSSEIN'?

The practice of giving names to hurricanes was begun by Clement Wragge, a meteorologist at the Queensland Weather Centre, Australia, in the early 20th century. He gave them the names of persons he particularly disliked – but modern practice is to take the names in succession from an alphabetical list of common forenames.

THE US NAVY IS DEFEATED

In December 1944, the US Navy's Third Fleet, perhaps the most powerful naval force ever assembled, was driven from the Pacific and forced to retire to its base for repairs. What the might of the Imperial Japanese Navy had failed to do was accomplished by a typhoon. On 18 December, off Luzon, Philippines, the great storm sank three destroyers, severely damaged a cruiser and eight aircraft carriers, destroyed 186 aircraft, and killed 759 sailors. Admiral William 'Bull' Halsey, accused of ignoring warnings from his meteorologists, later had to face a court of inquiry into the disaster.

GONE WITH THE WINDS

THE CARIBBEAN and the southern states of the USA are the areas where hurricanes are most destructive in terms of cost. As early as August 1667, colonists in Jamestown, Virginia, reported deaths and destruction caused by 'the dreadful Hurry Cane'. The 'Great Hurricane' of 1780 ravaged the Caribbean for eight days, killing 20-30,000 people: including 4,000 sailors and marines of the French fleet, which lost some 40 ships at Martinique.

After losing 250 inhabitants to a hurricane that levelled their town in August 1886, the second time it had been razed by winds, the people of Indianola, Texas, simply packed up and abandoned the site.

In terms of loss of life, the USA's worst natural disaster was the hurricane that struck Galveston, Texas, a major port on the Gulf of Mexico, on the evening of 8 September 1900. Built on a low-lying island, Galveston suffered not only the mayhem created by the winds, but also severe flooding from surges driven by 160-195km/h (100-120mph) gusts. In a few hours (during which an estimated 25cm/10in of rain fell), gale and flood had destroyed much of the city,

killing some 6,000 of its 37,000 inhabitants; about the same number were killed elsewhere along the Gulf Coast. Looting was rampant: a malefactor said to have been found with 23 rings – still on severed fingers – was among those summarily executed when martial law was declared. Hurricane warning systems throughout the USA were established a result of the disaster. At Galveston itself, a massive seawall (now 16km/10mi long) was built to protect the city – but on 16 August 1915 another hurricane breached it, and 275 people died.

HURRICANE GILBERT

In the last week of September 1989, only a few days after Hurricane David had lashed the area, killing 1,200 people in

Above: Damage caused by Hurricane Andrew.

NEW TROUSERS AFTER ANDREW!

Hurricane Andrew, said to have been the most costly natural disaster in the history of the USA, ravaged the Bahamas, southern Florida and Louisiana – where plans were made to evacuate the entire city of New Orleans – in the last week of August 1992. Winds of more than 257km/h (160mph) tore apart mobile homes (common in the region), ripped yachts from their moorings and mashed them against piers, and hoisted vehicles onto the roofs of buildings. To curb looting in the Miami area, where all public services were off-line for many days, riot police and 15,000 National Guardsmen were deployed and Federal troops placed on standby. More than 50 people were killed, and overall damage was estimated at up to $20 billion. Bruce Powers of Miami summed up Andrew's impact succinctly: 'I hope I die if I'm ever that afraid again. We all dirtied our pants.'

the Dominican Republic – and almost exactly on the first anniversary of the destructive Hurricane Gilbert, which gusted up to a western hemisphere record of 350km/h (218mph) – the Caribbean and American South suffered a 3,700km (2,300mi) swathe of carnage inflicted by Hurricane Hugo, gusting at up to 225km/h (140mph).

In the Virgin Islands, destruction was so great and subsequent looting so widespread that President Bush committed 1,200 military police, US marshals and FBI agents to restore order. But in all affected areas, fewer than 50 persons were killed by Hugo; a tribute to the efficacy of modern warning systems and emergency services. In North and South Carolina, state authorities evacuated threatened areas ahead of the storm. But among the many buildings destroyed or extensively damaged, to a cost estimated at some $4 billion, was historic Fort Sumter, Charleston, South Carolina, flashpoint of the American Civil War, which suffered damage put at $1,000,000. A more modern military installation nearby was even worse hit: damage to the US Air Force Base, where aircraft were hurled around like a child's toys, was described by the Pentagon as 'catastrophic'.

Above: Two views of Galveston, Texas, after it was struck by a hurricane in September 1886.

73

DIVINE AND DEVILISH WINDS

THE SUICIDAL servicemen who mounted a last-ditch defence of Japan during World War II, attacking Allied ships with crash-diving aircraft, 'human torpedoes' and similar weapons, were honoured with the name kamikaze ('divine wind'). The term dated back to 1274 and 1281, when heaven-sent typhoons destroyed Mongol invasion fleets off Japan. Japan has, however, had little cause to honour other typhoons, which seem to have been sent by evil spirits rather than raised by the Shinto gods.

The typhoon of 26 September 1954 was not the worst to strike the Japanese islands, but it is vividly remembered in Hakodate, on southern Hokkaido island, where it took 1,600 lives. Most died in a single incident: steaming from Hokkaido to Honshu island, the ferry *Toyu Maru* (4,400 tonnes) came directly within the eye-wall (the area of extreme turbulence surrounding the 'eye') of the typhoon and, its engines failing, was wrecked on a reef. Not one of its 1,172 passengers survived.

TYPHOON VERA

Japan's worst-ever typhoon, Typhoon Vera, struck central Honshu on 26-27 September 1959. Winds of up to 220km/h (135mph) battered the coastline from the Tokyo area to Nagoya in the south. The port of Nagoya, site of a famous castle, built in 1612 and in 1959 newly reconstructed after bomb-damage in World War II when the city's industries were a prime target, and of the revered Atsuta and Ise Shrines, was struck at high tide. Twenty-one ships were driven ashore, including a 7,500-tonne freighter, the *Changsha*. Wind-

driven waves raged over the seawalls into adjacent timber yards, turning heavy logs into deadly missiles that 'torpedoed' buildings – many already stripped of their roofs by the raving wind. Within a few hours, about one-third of the city lay under flood – waters in which the bodies of folk drowned in their own homes floated; elsewhere, rubble strewed the streets. Some 25,000 homeless, hungry

people roamed the streets – so did looters, forcing the enrollment of a 1,100-strong auxiliary police force. Because all services had failed, many persons drank polluted water, resulting in outbreaks of dysentery and typhus.

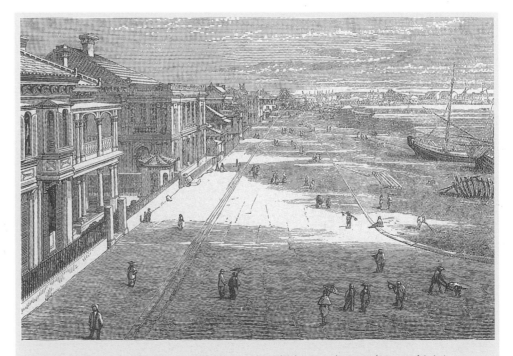

Above: Kōbe, Japan, before a typhoon in 1871 which caused great damage (right).

74

RIDERS ON THE STORMS

In the USA, advanced warning of severe storms is provided by the University of Oklahoma's CAPS (Center for the Analysis and Prediction of Storms) which, aided by its supercomputer ARPS (Advanced Regional Prediction System), claims 80 per cent accuracy for its local predictions. ARPS incorporates information from NOAA (National Oceanic and Atmospheric Administration) geostationary weather satellites, which track typhoons and hurricanes from their origin in low-pressure oceanic areas. 'Storm chasers' – like Europe's FASTEX (Front and Atlantic Storm Track Experiment) team – fly to the sites of developing storms and then ride along with them to record their behaviour.

Right: A cyclone, the low-pressure area that causes typhoons, photographed from space.

BODIES CARRIED OUT TO SEA

The overall toll of Typhoon Vera, which caused significant damage in 38 of Japan's 47 provinces, was put at more than 5,000 dead – many bodies were never recovered, having been carried out to sea – and more than 32,000 injured. Some 40,000 homes were destroyed. Crops were lost over about 2,070sq km (800sq mi) of agricultural land, where rice paddies contaminated with seawater would take years to recover, and several thousand head of livestock perished. As they had done after World War II, the Japanese people spent little time bewailing their misfortune, but set to work to repair the damage of yet another blow from the malign heavens.

AUSTRALIA'S HOLIDAY OF HORROR

THE CITY of Darwin, capital of Australia's Northern Territory and a major port on the Timor Sea, is no stranger to disaster. Since the first settlers arrived in what was then called Palmerston in 1862, Darwin has been almost completely destroyed on no less than six occasions.

During the rainy season (November-March), when most of the annual rainfall of around 150cm (59in) is delivered in a few torrential downpours, it is regularly visited by tropical cyclones. Those of 1878, 1882, 1897 and 1937 levelled the city's buildings, with some loss of life. The people of Darwin, tough gold-miners, pearl fishermen, crocodile hunters and stockmen with a legendary reputation for drinking and brawling, were not to be moved. They rebuilt – as they did after repeated Japanese air attacks again razed most of Darwin, then an important military base, during World War II. But the sixth, and worst, blow was still to come.

In a tropical city with average temperatures ranging between 20-30°C (68-86°F), no one among Darwin's 47,000 citizens was expecting a White Christmas in 1974 – but nor were they anticipating a holiday of horror. The unwanted guest at the feast was Cyclone Tracy, Australia's worst-ever storm, first reported by Darwin's Tropical Cyclone Warning Centre on 21 December, as it brewed up over the Arafura Sea, some 480km (300mi) to the northeast.

UNWANTED CHRISTMAS GIFT

Cyclone Tracy, with wind speeds recorded at up to 217km/h (135mph), struck Darwin in the early hours of Christmas Day. By 0100 hours, most power lines were down: citizens crouched in pitch darkness – until the raging gale let in more light by tearing off the roofs of their houses. Cars and pickups, and light aircraft at the airport, were tossed around like a child's scale models. At around dawn the winds dropped, but those who ventured out from shelter to view the devastation soon regretted their temerity: the calm was caused by the 'eye' of the cyclone passing over Darwin – and the winds swiftly returned.

In all, the storm raged for about five hours. When it had passed, nine-tenths of Darwin lay in ruins: almost every building had been destroyed or badly damaged. Sixty-five people had been killed and most of the survivors were homeless. Such was the chaos that the many of the injured could not be treated locally; medical evacuations by air began almost immediately, followed by mass air and road evacuation of the homeless.

BLACK DAYS DOWN UNDER

As well as the 'Christmas Cyclone', Australia remembers three other unpleasant anniversaries, all commemorating horrendous bushfires. On 'Black Thursday', 6 February 1851, during a heatwave in which shade temperature in Melbourne reached 47°C (117°F), fires driven by strong northerly winds ravaged much of the state of Victoria, killing at least 10 persons and destroying thousands of head of stock and many homes. 'Black Friday', 13 January 1939, again saw fires raging throughout Victoria: several townships were destroyed and 71 people were killed. Among Australia's worst bushfires were those of 'Ash Wednesday', 16 February 1983, when heat, drought, high winds – and, it is said, the work of fire-raising vandals – sent fires sweeping through large areas of Victoria and South Australia. More than 2,000 houses were destroyed, 72 people were killed, and damage was estimated at around $400,000,000.

Within a week, more 25,000 persons had left. Darwin was a ghost town. It looked, said an aerial observer, 'like Hiroshima after the atomic bomb'.

PIONEERING SPIRIT

Once more, however, the spirit of the frontier pioneers triumphed. A Darwin Reconstruction Committee was formed, and within three years the city had been rebuilt. So well was this task accomplished, with new cyclone-proof buildings along streets laid out on a compact, pedestrian-friendly grid system, that the city has since grown rapidly: at the last census, in 1993, its population had reached nearly 78,000.

All Pictures: Cyclones are a constant threat in tropical areas of the world, where they often inflict severe damage to property.

77

DESTRUCTION IN THE DELTA

I N NOVEMBER 1970, a cyclone warning aroused little concern in Bangladesh (then East Pakistan). In a monsoon country regularly blasted by tropical cyclones, people become hardened to the peril. The subsistence-level farmers and fishermen who make up a large part of the population cannot afford to leave their homes or work at every storm alert – and, in any case, there is little refuge from cyclone-driven seas to be found in the low-lying Ganges delta area.

In 1970, moreover, alarms some three weeks earlier of a major cyclone had proved false. Thus, although the storm's progress was tracked by satellite on its way to Bangladesh, when the cyclone hit it caught most of the closely packed population (around 390 per sq km/1,000 per sq mi) unprepared.

Funnelling down the Bay of Bengal at upwards of 160km/h (100mph), the cyclone generated massive waves 6-15m (20-50ft) high. Wind and water hit the offshore islands with a mighty roar, smashing houses and sweeping their sleeping occupants out to sea. Manpura Island vanished under water which rose 6m (20ft) above the high tide mark, sweeping all but four of its 4,500 bamboo houses out of existence. On the 70km (43mi) long Dakhin Shahbaz (Bhola) Island, largest in the delta, 200,000 people drowned: one-fifth of its population.

The storm moved on over the mainland. Over an area of 7,770sq km (3,000sq mi) houses were flattened and fields swamped; about 75 per cent of the staple rice crop was destroyed, along with many fishing boats. The overall death toll was estimated between

300,000 and 500,000: the wind-driven flood waters had left corpses hanging in trees like bundles of rags; every hour, the Bay of Bengal gave up more dead,

sweeping in their bodies to pile up on the shore. One villager said: 'We have buried 5,000 in mass graves... We can't dig any more.' Despite foreign aid, many who had survived the storm later perished from exposure, starvation or disease, for, with no fresh water to drink, typhoid and cholera spread rapidly.

RAGING TIDAL WAVES

In May 1985 the islands of the Ganges delta were hit once more by the combination of cyclone and sea. Winds of more than 160km/h (100mph) and raging tidal waves killed 10,000 persons, flattened 80 per cent of the region's

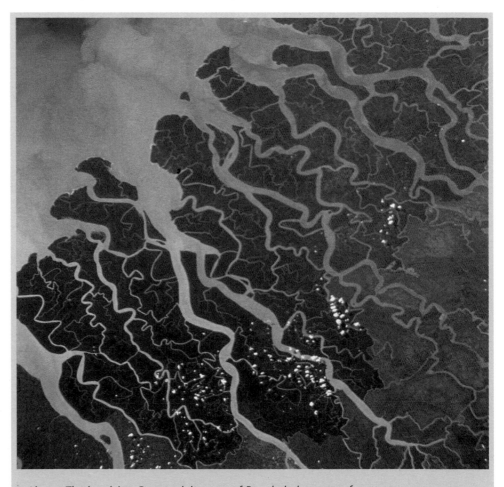

Above: The low-lying Ganges delta area of Bangladesh, as seen from space.

houses and drowned 500,000 cattle. As thousands of helpless people were swept into the sea, some apparently fortunate refugees managed to reach purpose-built concrete cyclone shelters – only to drown there as the waves flooded their refuge. Once again the storm had been tracked by satellite, but no official warning was broadcast in Bangladesh.

Over an eight-hour period on 30 April 1991, a giant cyclone hit Bangladesh's southeast coast. Winds gusting at up to 233km/h (145mph) smashed houses, ripped up trees and power lines, and battered to death hundreds of people. With the cyclone came seismic waves which ravaged the important port of Chittagong, washed away whole villages, destroyed 5,000 fishing boats in the Bay of Bengal, and again swamped the rice fields. Some 70,000 persons were estimated to have died. On this occasion, cyclone warnings were issued on television – a luxury available to few of the population, who had in any case been

Above: A tropical rainstorm stirs the trees.
Right: Damage caused by a severe cyclone.

lulled into a false sense of security by 11 consecutive mistaken storm alarms. International rescue teams found the roofs of the few buildings left standing crowded with desperate refugees; below them, the water was choked with bodies. In the next month, a tornado and a minor earthquake added to the survivors' misery.

THE MURDEROUS MONSOONS

Even when the region is spared cyclones, Bangladesh and its neighbour India regularly suffer flooding caused by torrential rains. The southwest monsoon wind prevailing in the Indian Ocean in April-October usually brings heavy rains – sometimes too heavy. In recent years, monsoon rains have flooded Bangladesh in 1974 (2,000 dead; millions homeless) and 1988. In the latter case, deforestation of the Himalayas also contributed to flooding that covered 75 per cent of the country; up to 5,000 persons died. Northern India was swamped by monsoonal rains in September 1978, when more than 5,180sq km (2,000sq mi) of crops were destroyed and about 15,000 people are believed to have drowned.

TWISTERS IN 'TORNADO ALLEY'

ALTHOUGH A few countries suffer more frequently from 'twisters', the USA has the greatest incidence of severe tornadoes, those classified at 4 or 5 on the 1-5 Fujita Scale. The most perilous region is 'Tornado Alley', running across Missouri, Kansas (remember how Dorothy was blown 'over the rainbow' to the Land of Oz!), Oklahoma and Texas. Every year, spring and early summer bring the 'tornado season' that Midwesterners have good reason to dread.

St. Louis, Missouri, was the first large American city to experience a major tornado: in a 20-minute storm on 27 May 1896, more than 300 persons died and around 2,500 were injured; property damage amounted to $12,000,000 – then a huge sum. In late March 1923, a series of twisters travelled 470km (292mi) across the Midwest in four days, killing 211 people. Missouri was again severely hit by the tornadoes of 18 March 1925: at Annapolis, a twister completely wrecked a 300m (980ft) wide sector across the city, killing 823 people and injuring some 3,000. From De Soto, Missouri, the storms raced into Illinois, where the towns of Gorham and Murphysboro (where 150 of the city's 200 blocks of buildings were brought down, crushing to death 234 persons) were devastated to the sound of 'a roaring noise as of many trains'. The storms did not blow themselves out until they had moved on to destroy Griffin and Princeton in Indiana: their total toll was 689 dead, 2,000 injured and more than 15,000 homeless.

In more recent years, the Midwest has been hit by two particularly destructive tornado outbreaks. On 11 April 1965,

some 40 tornadoes, escorted by around 50 thunderstorms, ranged over the entire area, killing 271 people and damaging property in excess of $200,000,000. The worst outbreak since 1925 came on 2-3 April 1974, when within 18 hours 148 twisters touched down in an area extending from Alabama to the Canadian border.

TORNADO TERROR

The two towns worst hit were Xenia, Ohio, and Brandenburg, Kentucky. Loss of life there may have been greater because in the past Xenia had experienced few tornadoes – and Brandenburg had never seen one. During a five-minute stroll through Xenia at 64km/h (40mph), a twister tore to pieces timber-framed homes, hurled railroad cars from their tracks into the main street, and blocked roads with felled trees. Of the town's 27,000 inhabitants, 33 were killed and 1,600 injured; among the 1,300 buildings destroyed were 12 churches and six schools. In the small town of Brandenburg, the destruction of property was less but the horror greater, for the majority of the 29 dead were children from a school playground. Overall, 324 persons were killed by twisters.

EL NIÑO: PACIFIC PHENOMENON

Like the Florida tornadoes of February 1998, torrential rains that caused several deaths (see pages 82-83) and an estimated $450,000,000 damage in California in January-February 1998 – as well as other 'weather disasters' around the world in 1997–98 – were blamed on El Niño ('the [Christ] Child'; so-called because it appears in December around Christmas time). Every few years, this warm-water current that flows along the western coasts of Ecuador and Peru reaches an intensity that causes widespread climatic disturbances. At such times, El Niño's currents severely weaken or even reverse the prevailing east-to-west winds and change sea surface temperatures. The effect is to bring storms and heavy rains to South America and droughts to Southeast Asia and east and south Africa. Weather patterns in other areas are disturbed to a lesser but significant extent.

81

MICKEY MOUSE'S NARROW SQUEAK

Florida suffers more damage from hurricanes (see pages 72-73) than tornadoes – but the 'twisters' of 23 February 1998 were exceptional. Spinning from storm-winds triggered by the El Niño current, dozens of tornadoes rampaged across central Florida, demolishing mobile home parks, destroying vehicles and throwing communications into chaos. In spite of storm warnings, some 50 people died and many more were injured. But although tornadoes raged all around the Orlando area, home of Disney World and other crowded tourist attractions, Mickey Mouse and his visitors escaped harm.

Opposite and above: The awesome sight of a massive 'twister' is an all-too-frequent spectre on the horizon of the American Midwest's 'Tornado Alley'.

Below: Damage caused by a Texan tornado.

THE PERILOUS PEAKS OF PERU

THE BRITISH writer Claud Cockburn claimed to have produced the most banal newspaper headline of all time: 'Small Earthquake in Chile; Not Many Dead'. Had he been writing of Chile's northern neighbour, Peru, and without humorous intent, he might have come up with a more gruesome heading: 'Huge Landslide in Peru; Thousands Dead' – for of the ten worst landslides and avalanches recorded in the 20th century, four have occurred in the mountainous regions that cover the greater part of the country.

Most landslides and mudslides, and many avalanches, are triggered either by earthquakes or by volcanic eruptions. In 1941, an earthquake in west central Peru sent an avalanche from the Andean peaks of the Cordillera Blanca crashing down into the valley of Callejón de Huaylas, almost levelling the market town of Huarás and killing 5,000 persons (about half its total population). An identical occurrence wiped out the mining settlement of Chungar, some 3,050m (10,000ft) up in the high Andes, on 19 March 1971, when the estimated death toll ranged between 400 and 600.

THE MALEVOLENT GIANT

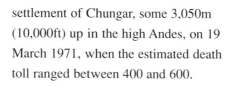

Peru's highest point, at 6,768m (22,205ft), is the major summit of the Huascarán massif (Nevado de Huascarán), an inactive volcanic formation in the Andean Cordillera Blanca. Huascarán has been the malevolent giant whose missiles have taken most lives in Peru's most recent disasters. Unusually mild weather late in 1961, along with very heavy snowfalls, combined to fracture Huascarán's Glacier 511. On 10 January 1962, some 3,000,000 tonnes of snow and ice roared down into the Callejón de Huaylas, sweeping with it four mountain villages, along with shepherds and their flocks, from the lower slopes. Then, reaching more level ground, it formed a solid 'tidal wave' some 18m (60ft) high and advanced at around 96km/h (60mph) on the town of Ranrahirca, which, with almost all its 2,700 inhabitants, it near-obliterated. The total death toll of the 1962 avalanche was estimated at 3,500.

Below: Destruction of adobe houses in Huarás, Peru. Rubble and debris fills the street as the result of an earthquake.

Above: Villagers flee from an avalanche.

citizens were entombed by the landslide, swallowed up by earthquake fissures, or drowned by floods caused by the bursting of dams on lakes in the high Andes. The overall toll exacted by the landslide alone was reckoned at 25,000 dead, making it the worst disaster of its kind ever recorded.

Left: An overturned bus on top of avalanche debris at the site of the former Plaza de Armas, Yungay, Peru.
Below: This large boulder, estimated to weigh 700 tonnes, was carried by the Huascarán avalanche in May 1970. It has come to rest on top of a layer of drying mud.

A MASSIVE SHOCK

That figure was far eclipsed by the share claimed for Huascarán's part in Peru's worst natural disaster – the earthquake of 31 May 1970. Stemming from a fault on the seabed about 24km (15mi) off the Pacific coast, a massive shock registering 7.75 on the Richter Scale claimed some 70,000 lives throughout western Peru, with 50,000 injured and 200,000 made homeless. In the throes of the quake, Huascarán shrugged off an estimated 68,814,000cu m (90,000,000cu yd) of ice, snow, rock and mud. Descending at a rate of around 320km/h (200mph) from an altitude of 3,660m (12,000ft), the mighty landslide covered some 11km (7mi) of level ground in the Callejón de Huaylas, engulfing all that remained of Ranrahirca and its neighbouring villages after the disaster of 1962 and burying the nearby city of Yungay under a pall of debris up to 12m (40ft) deep. An estimated 17,500 of Yungay's 20,000

CALIFORNIA – NOT COLD, BUT IT'S DAMP

Torrential rains that hit California in January-February 1998 were blamed on the influence of El Niño. As well as property damage estimated at around $450,000,000, the storms claimed several lives. On 25 February 1998, at least 10 persons were reported killed by mudslides, which pushed houses off their foundations, and other rain-induced incidents. North of Los Angeles, the rain-swollen Cuyama River gouged a 213m (700ft) chasm along Highway 166, swallowing up a California Highway Patrol car and its two occupants.

THE THUNDERING THREAT

AVALANCHES ARE typically caused when a sudden heavy snowfall, or a thaw beneath a thick covering of older snow, destroys the coherence of the mass of snow on a slope (usually one of 30° or more). As well as temperature, they may be triggered by loud noises or chance vibrations – a thunderstorm, a sudden gale, the passing of a skier may set off an avalanche.

Even a minor avalanche may imperil mountain villages, herdsmen and winter sports enthusiasts. An avalanche monitored in Switzerland achieved a speed of 346km/h (215mph) and covered 6.9km (4.3mi), hurdling about 1.6km (1mi) of level ground in a valley bottom, in 72 seconds; thus, the destructive potential of a major avalanche, carrying perhaps 50,000,000 tonnes or more of snow and ice, is obviously immense.

INVISIBLE HAZARD

The natural disasters described throughout this book are, to say the least, hard to ignore: but a natural hazard that goes largely unnoticed is, it is claimed, taking many lives every year. This is radon, a radioactive gas formed by the decay of uranium minerals, which may seep up from the ground. Where concentrated areas of the gas exist, its effect can be deadly: it is estimated that in Britain alone about 2,500 people die every year die from radon-induced lung cancer. A laboratory-made isotope, however, called Radon-222, can be beneficial – it is used in the treatment of some forms of cancer.

The Carthaginian general Hannibal, marching his armies into Italy in 218 BC, is said to have lost 18,000 men and 2,000 horses to a series of avalanches (perhaps set off by the heavy tread of his famous war elephants) in the Italian Alpine passes. In World War I, avalanches became a major weapon: in the 1915–18 campaign in the Tyrolean Alps, both Italian and Austrian gunners attempted to entomb their opponents under avalanches deliberately triggered by artillery fire: it is estimated that some 40,000 soldiers perished beneath the snows.

SEVERE AVALANCHES

In the Swiss Alps, in January-April 1951, a combination of heavy snowfalls and howling blizzards, depositing a thick layer of damp, unstable snow on existing, firmer snow cover, led to the record occurrence of some 130 severe avalanches. The overall death toll in Switzerland, Italy, Austria and France was estimated at a minimum of 280 persons; wildlife suffered heavily, and in forests preserved as avalanche breaks about 65sq km (25sq mi) of trees were levelled.

The worst avalanche disaster of recent years was the double blow suffered by the small town of Blons and the nearby

LOST IN 'WEEPING WATERS'

A lahar (mudslide caused by volcanic action) triggered one of New Zealand's worst disasters. Lava from the 2,800m (9,180ft)-high volcano Mount Ruapehu, on North Island, had formed a natural dam around a mountain lake. On the night of 24 December 1953, the dam gave way, releasing a monster flow of mud, water, rocks, ice and ash into the Whangaehu River, which swiftly rose into a raging flood. Its waters swept away the central span of the Tangiwai ('Weeping Waters') railway bridge – shortly before the Wellington-Auckland night express was due to cross. The locomotive and five of the train's nine coaches plunged into the river: of 285 persons aboard the express, 151 were killed.

mining settlement of Leduc, near the Arlberg Pass in Austria's Rhaetian Alps, on 11 January 1954. One avalanche struck in mid-morning, destroying about 25 per cent of Blons; in the early evening, as survivors struggled to dig out neighbours buried in rubble and snow, a second avalanche arrived to complete the destruction. In Blons, 111 of its 376 inhabitants died; at Leduc, 300 miners were entombed. About 30 persons survived by digging themselves out of the snow; some 30 more were extricated alive by rescuers, some after being buried for nearly three days.

Right: Avalanche of snow in northern Italy.

DROUGHT, FAMINE AND FIRE

LATE IN 1997, British scientists warned that because of changes to river ecology caused by global warming, the water resources of southern and eastern England could drop by 25 per cent within 20 years. The press spoke of 'drought' – but British people, although perhaps irked by restrictions on the use of garden hoses, are unlikely to experience the deadly effects of true drought, which brings in its train the further disasters of famine and, often, fire.

bodyweight, might have a chance to survive. 'And,' he stated, 'the ones who make it to this camp are the strong ones – the others are dying up in the hills, too weak to move.'

Spectacular efforts to help, like Sir Bob Geldof's open-air Live Aid concert, which raised £50,000,000, focused world attention on the 'hungry continent' of Africa, where more than 150,000,000

Droughts, properly defined as periods of abnormally dry weather at a time when rains might be expected, particularly affect such areas as the Sahel of west Africa, fringing the arid Sahara, which experienced prolonged drought and savage famine in the period 1968–80, and similar desert fringe regions. The most severe drought and famine in recent years was experienced in Ethiopia in 1982–85 (with further suffering from the same cause being experienced in 1987 and the earlier 1990s). After several months without rain, crops failed all over the north and east of the country – which was already torn apart by civil war. An estimated 5,000,000 victims of drought joined tens of thousand of war refugees in the rush to relief camps unable to cope with such numbers. By October 1984, in spite of international aid, some 1,000 Ethiopians were dying of starvation each week. Close on half Ethiopia's 42,000,000 million people were suffering from malnourishment; about 2,500,000 had been forced into a life of nomadic food-gathering.

The director of a British-run children's aid centre revealed that his staff, unable to feed all who came, had decided to give priority to those who, *having lost no more than 70 per cent of their normal*

Above: People beg for food in a street in Bombay, India, during a famine in 1900.

86

people were threatened by starvation in the mid-1980s. In Chad, drought had been proportionally worse than in Ethiopia; in Mozambique, years of drought were followed by hurricanes and floods. In several countries, on-going guerrilla warfare and political rivalry hindered aid efforts. So many refugees from Ethiopia and Chad entered Sudan that a lesser but still severe famine, along with political destabilization, was caused there.

DROUGHT AND FIRE

The western USA is another area much affected by drought, although there the concomitant danger is not famine, but fire. A four-year drought in the later 1980s, along with scorching temperatures and dry thunderstorms, saw fires ravaging the forests and grasslands of the American West in August 1989, when Idaho reported 43 major fires burning simultaneously and National Guardsmen were called in to help 9,000 fire fighters. In 1988, and again in 1990, forest fires

triggered by lightning strikes in bone-dry brush threatened to destroy California's famous Yosemite National Park. In 1990, despite the efforts of some 15,000 firefighters, about 100sq km (39sq mi) of Yosemite's forest were destroyed. Overall, the West lost more than 14,500sq km (5,600sq mi) of forest to fires in 1990.

A HOT TIME IN SYDNEY

Bush fires, attributed to lightning after long periods of drought and high temperatures, have twice threatened the city of Sydney, Australia, in recent years. In January 1994 bush fires ringed the city for seven days, killing four persons, injuring more than 400, destroying or badly damaging 300 dwellings, and devastating 8,100sq km (3,125sq mi) of farmland. On 8 December 1997, a sudden downpour of rain and the onset of cooler weather ended a 10-day bushfire emergency that threatened the city's suburbs. It was estimated that throughout New South Wales more than 400 separate fires had raged simultaneously, destroying more than 3,900sq km (1,550sq mi) of forests in the state.

Above left: Many areas of Africa, such as the Sahel which fringes the Sahara desert, are subject to prolonged drought and famine. Below: A forest fire threatens homes.

87

IRELAND'S ORDEAL BY FAMINE

'WE HAVE made Ireland…the most degraded and the most miserable country in the world.' Lord John Russell (1792–1878), speaking in the House of Lords in March 1846, was one of the few powerful Englishmen to express sympathy – and a degree of guilt – for the tragic plight of the Irish people in the famine years of 1845–51, although when he became Prime Minister later that year, he did little to relieve Ireland's suffering.

All too many Englishmen agreed with Sir Charles Trevelyan (1807–86), Secretary of the Treasury: 'The great evil…is not the physical evil of the famine, but the moral evil of the selfish, perverse and turbulent character of the people.'

The potato, easy and cheap to cultivate, store and cook, rich in vitamins B and C and essential minerals, was introduced to Ireland during the 17th century. In a country where political troubles (and laws that 'protected' British agricultural industries against Irish

competition) inhibited large-scale agriculture, 'praties' or 'Murphys' rapidly became the staple food of the peasantry, the poorer country folk (and the majority) of the population. They appeared to thrive on it: in the early 19th century, the population grew at record rate, reaching 8,200,000 in 1841. (In 1991, the total population of Ireland, including Ulster, was 5,103,719.) It is estimated that for at least one-third of this number, the potato supplied 80 per cent of their calorific intake.

Then, in the damp July of 1845, the potato blight (the fungus *Phytophthora*

Below: The potato blight spread to Ireland in 1845, causing widespread famine.

infestans), first appearing in North America and swiftly spreading to Europe, came to Ireland. Peasants who had looked with satisfaction at their fertile fields in the evening woke next morning to the stench of rot, as their potato plants putrefied in the grip of what was graphically called 'potato cholera'. Thus began 'the Great Hunger'. By autumn 1845, deaths from starvation had begun. The British government marginally improved its poor-relief schemes, but its general policy was that the Irish should help themselves – and British exploitation had taken so much wealth from Ireland that this was impossible

REPORTS OF CANNIBALISM

In 1846 the crop failed once more; the harvest of 1847 was fairly sound, but low in yield; in 1848, the blight struck again. From rural areas, there were reports of entire villages dying, with corpses lying unburied in the streets; of families living on grass, chewing clay to counterfeit the sensation of full bellies; even of cannibalism. Tens of thousands of peasants sought shelter in the workhouses of the towns, where epidemics of the diseases most closely associated with famine – typhus, cholera, dysentery – killed those who had survived starvation. When the Irish protested England's reluctance to aid them, the British government's response was massively to reinforce its military garrisons and to impose martial law in some areas.

The blight did not return in 1849, and by 1851 food supplies had returned to normal. But in just six years, the population of Ireland had been reduced by some 2,000,000-2,500,000. It is estimated that between 800,000 and 1,000,000 starved to death: the rest

emigrated, mainly to the USA. In 1847–1861, more than 2,000,000 Irish emigrants entered North America, in one of the most significant (in the long term) population movements in history.

THE LEGACY OF FAMINE

People debilitated by starvation are particularly open to the *Rickettsia* bacteria, spread by lice, which causes typhus, a killer of tens of thousands during the Irish and other famines. This ancient plague – the 'Plague of Thucydides' that decimated Athens in 431–427 BC is believed to have been a hybrid of typhus and measles – flourishes in dirty, crowded environments. Thus, it has at various times been called 'gaol fever', 'ship fever', 'camp fever' (as such, a major killer during the American Civil War), and, in World Wars I and II, 'trench fever'. The worst-ever typhus epidemic, in the chaos of revolutionary Russia in 1917–21, is believed to seen 25,000,000 sufferers. of whom 2,500,000 died. A threatened epidemic in Naples in the winter of 1943–44 was averted by dusting more than 3,200,000 persons with the insecticide DDT.

Above: Peasants begging for food during the famine in Russia. The worst-ever typhus epidemic occurred In revolutionary Russia between 1917 and 1921, when an estimated 2,500,000 sufferers died of the disease.

THE GREAT PLAINS BLEW AWAY

FOR MANY centuries, the Great Plains of the American West where the buffalo roamed sustained the way of life of Native American hunters. In the later 19th century, buffalo and 'redskin' alike were destroyed or driven out by white settlers, who proceeded to transform the area into an agricultural cornucopia. Ranchers ran vast herds of cattle without further significant harm to the Plains' ecology – but then 'sodbusters', crop-growing farmers, moved in. With the improvement of agricultural technology in the earlier 20th century, huge areas of the Plains' 'sea of grass' were ploughed for the intensive cultivation of wheat and other crops.

By the 1920s, Plains' farmers had noticed that the high winds common to the region often raised dust-storms, snatching up the rich but light topsoil that was no longer anchored by the strong root system of its original grass, and which was further weakened by over-intensive cultivation. Then, from 1934 (when the Midwest went ten months without rain) to 1937, the region endured a succession of droughts. Crops were ruined – the normally lush wheatfields looked, said a government adviser, 'like stubble on an old man's chin' – and the loosened soil, baked by summer temperatures which often rose above 38°C (100°F) mark, was whisked away in 'black blizzards'.

THE DUST BOWL

The worst-hit area, about 388,500sq km (150,000sq mi) of the southern Great Plains, extending over west Kansas, Oklahoma, east Colorado and the Texas panhandle, became known as 'the Dust Bowl'. Whole farms literally blew away, losing up to 4in (10cm) of topsoil. Dust storms were so all-pervading that in the Midwest roads were blocked, dwellings buried and livestock choked to death; the

90

Above: The Great Plains of the American West were home both to Native American Indians and the vast herds of buffalo that they hunted.

Above: A Midwest farmer harvests spring wheat under the glare of a sweltering Sun.

THE SWELTERING SUMMERS

The USA's hottest summers to date have been those of 1980 and 1981. In 1980, at least 1,200 persons, most in the Midwest and South, died from heat in June-July. In Dallas, Texas, temperatures exceeded 38°C (100°F) for 23 days in succession. Many farmers and ranchers were ruined, as crops parched and the price of fodder rocketed. Brush and forest fires (see also pages 86-87) raged and, as police have come to expect, the sultry weather saw a notable increase in violent crime. In 1981, a record temperature of 49.4°C (121°F) was recorded at Red Bluff, California.

crops that did survive on the ground were killed by dust. Skies as far away as Washington D.C. took on the hue of thunderclouds; red dust settled on the snows of the New England states; dust clouds even enveloped ships some 480km (300mi) off the Atlantic coast.

Many thousand farmers and their families – up to 60 per cent of the Dust Bowl's population – dispossessed because of debt or simply 'blown away', trekked westward in search of a livelihood. Most headed for the rich farmlands of California, only to find that penniless 'Okies' (an estimated 300,000 fled from Oklahoma alone), or 'Exodusters', were not welcomed by their more fortunate countrymen. The sufferings of the migrants are memorably recorded in John Steinbeck's novel *The Grapes of Wrath* (1939), in the songs of Woodrow Wilson ('Woody') Guthrie (1912–67) and in the *American Exodus* (1939) photographs by Dorothea Lange (1895–1965).

Although little was done to help the migrants, the 'New Deal' policies of the later 1930s helped to re-establish those farmers who had managed to stay put, and sought to prevent another Dust Bowl disaster. Farmers were subsidized to plant trees and grass to anchor the soil, to leave certain areas uncultivated each year, and to plough and terrace along the land's natural contours so as to hold rainwater. Even so, another severe drought in the 1950s caused dust storms that persuaded the government further to subsidize the conversion of many million acres into grassland.

KILLING HEAT

The great droughts of the 1930s also saw a significant number of deaths from pneumonia, due to inhalation of dust, and heat-stroke. It is estimated that some 15,000 Americans died of heat-stroke in the years 1934–36. Unfeeling people relished a joke about an 'Okie' who fainted when a raindrop fell on his head – but was revived with two buckets of sand!

Above: Brush and forest fires are common in the Midwest during summer droughts.

'THE CRUELTY OF HEAVEN'

'I BURIED MY five children with my own hands. …and so many died that all believed it was the end of the world.' The children of Agnolo di Tura of Siena, Italy, were at least fortunate in that they received a decent burial. In the years of the Black Death, approximately the period 1345–50, thousands of corpses lay rotting in the streets of many of the world's largest cities: there was no one to bury them, for their relatives, friends and priests were themselves dying, dead – or fleeing in panic to a supposedly safe area.

The pandemic later known as the Black Death (from the dark colour of sufferers' bodies, caused by haemorrhages beneath the skin) probably originated in central Asia. How it spread worldwide was not fully understood until 1894, when it was established that the plague bacillus, *Yersinia*, is a disease of rodents, notably the black rat, and is spread by their fleas, which transfer to humans when their original host dies. It is probable that in the 14th century the disease was exported from Asia by rats infesting Italian trading ships.

By 1347, the plague was ravaging Italy and the Byzantine Empire. In 1348–49 it struck the Arab world: 40 per cent of the population of Cairo died, and Islamic writers say that at least one-third of all Muslims perished. From Italy the scourge swept into France, then into England, where estimates of the dead range between 1,000,000 and 2,000,000 (between one-quarter and one-half of the total population), Germany and Scandinavia. Throughout Europe, towns were depopulated, crops rotted in the fields, livestock died (the plague killed animals as well as humans) and law and morality collapsed. Estimates of the overall death toll vary: 75,000,000 worldwide is a figure often quoted. Deaths in Europe are believed to have been in the region of 25,000,000, or about one-third of the total population.

THE BLACK DEATH

Three types of plague made up the Black Death. Bubonic plague, so called from the swellings ('buboes') that form in the sufferer's armpits, throat and groin, normally killed 75 per cent of those stricken within one week. Even more deadly were septicaemic plague, in which plague bacilli entered the bloodstream and which killed within 24 hours, and pneumonic plague, affecting the lungs and easily spread by coughs and sneezes, mortal in up to 95 per cent of cases. Not until the development of sulphonamide drugs in the 1930s were there effective cures for these scourges. Medieval physicians variously blamed 'bad air' caused by earthquakes and volcanic eruptions, or even astrological influences, for the plague – and suggested treatments ranging from loud noises (to 'stir up' the air) to aromatherapy (sitting in smoke from bonfires), and abstention from rich foods, bathing and sexual intercourse.

Milan was one of the few cities to come near to controlling the disease: there, plague sufferers were walled up in their houses (along with any healthy folk who happened to be with them) – and less than 15 per cent of the population perished. In Florence, where no such draconian methods were adopted, the writer Giovanni Boccaccio estimated that 100,000 persons (equivalent to the city's total population) were struck down by 'the cruelty of heaven'. He reflected the

Church's view that the Black Death was God's punishment for the sins of humankind. Religious fanatics called Flagellants marched in bands through Europe, flogging each other as a sign of their repentance. The Flagellants led the way in blaming Jews for the pestilence: 12,000 Jews were massacred in Mainz in 1348, and there were mass lynchings in Strasbourg, Brussels, Frankfurt, Cologne and elsewhere.

THE KILLER STILL LURKS

The first major recorded outbreaks of bubonic plague are believed to have been the pestilences that struck Rome in AD 262, recorded as killing 5,000 persons per day, and Constantinople and the Middle East in the 6th century AD, when many millions are said to have died. The last major outbreak originated in Hong Kong in 1894. It quickly spread to India, where it is estimated to have killed more than 10,000,000 persons in c.1900–17. There have been limited epidemics in Asia and Africa in recent years, and isolated cases are still reported from every continent except Australia.

All pictures: Grim images of death by plague.

THE DEADLY 'SPANISH LADY'

THE MOST deadly plague ever to strike humankind, in terms of worldwide deaths within a comparatively short time, was the influenza pandemic (a plague that strikes all peoples) of 1918–19. Beginning in the final months of World War I, which claimed the lives of some 10,000,000 persons in four years, the influenza scourge accounted for nearly four times that number of victims – estimates range from 25,000,000 to 37,000,000 – inside 18 months.

Scientists did not isolate the Type A flu virus until 1933, but most agree that the illness has troubled mankind since the Greek 'father of medicine' Hippocrates (c.460–377 BC) described its classic symptoms: fever, chills, sore throat, headache, muscle pains, tiredness and dry coughing. It got its name from medieval Italian astrologers, who blamed it on the *influenza* (influence) of malign planets. The 1918–19 pandemic is generally known as 'Spanish Flu', or the 'Spanish Lady', since Spain was particularly hard-hit and, as a neutral country in World War I, did not censor news of the chaos caused by the outbreak. It had other names: German soldiers called it 'Blitz Catarrh'; English tommies suffered 'Flanders Grippe'; in Japan it was 'Wrestler's Fever'.

In fact, it originated in the USA where, according to genetic research in 1997, it was passed by birds to the animals on a pig farm in Iowa. Flu viruses pass easily between animals, most notably between pigs and poultry, and between infected animals and humans, mutating and becoming more virulent as they progress. Formerly, flu

did not pass quickly between humans, but modern high-speed transport between increasingly crowded urban centres means that it can now spread very rapidly, transferred by airborne droplets from coughs and sneezes. Modern airliners, where the air is continuously recirculated, provide an ideal playground for the virus.

SPANISH FLU

The first human sufferer from Spanish flu, in March 1918, appears to have been a soldier at Fort Riley, Kansas, where within two days a further 500 men were affected. The flu raced through barracks in the United States, jumped into troop ships, and swiftly invaded France. By

Right: Many peasants in Spain died from the terrible effects of influenza.

94

April it had reached the Far East; by May, Africa and South America. By August 1918 it had mutated to the point where it triggered off pneumonia in the lungs of those infected. It struck hardest at the 20-40 age group: at Camp Devens, Boston, some 8,000 of 45,000 soldiers died at the rate of 90 per day. A pathologist reported that the lungs of flu victims looked like 'red currant jelly'.

DEATH BY STARVATION

In the USA, Spanish flu killed an estimated 550,000 persons. In one of the worst-affected cities, Philadelphia, Pennsylvania, 158 out of every 1,000 citizens died. Elsewhere the death toll was even greater: in the South Pacific islands, where respiratory disease was uncommon, some 20 per cent of the population was wiped out; in Samoa, where 25 per cent of the population died, it was reported that many sick persons

succumbed not to flu, but to starvation, since there was no one fit enough to tend them. In Nome, Alaska, 60 per cent of the Eskimo community died. India lost some 5,000,000 persons (an estimated 4 per cent of its population); 200,000 persons died in the British Isles.

Since there were then no flu vaccines, people sought protection in various ways. Many cities banned public gatherings; regularly sprayed disinfectant on streets and public transport; or issued face masks

Above: A humorous drawing illustrating the 'benefits' of inoculation against 'cow-pock'.

(these were obligatory in San Francisco, where they were made free of charge by jeans-maker Levi Strauss). Folk remedies included cucumbers strapped to the legs, potatoes in pockets, an 'onion bath', and sulphur spread on the soles of shoes. Whether or not these measures had any effect, in April 1919 the flu vanished as suddenly as it had appeared.

FOWL PLAY IN HONG KONG

The major origin of modern flu viruses is China, where domestic fowls and pigs are intensively reared, sometimes under unhygienic conditions. In January 1998, the respected journal *Science* warned that the H5N1 flu virus appearing in Hong Kong in December 1997 could cause a pandemic like that of 1918–19, since it resembled that of the 'Spanish Lady'. The Hong Kong government immediately ordered the slaughter of all the estimated 1,300,000 chickens in the territory. At the time of writing, however, only a handful of humans had contracted 'Bird Flu'.

INDEX